Contents

Introduction

The contents of this book are based upon the National Science Education Standards for Grade 5. These standards include (A) Science as Inquiry, (B) Physical Science, (C) Life Science, (D) Earth and Space Science, (E) Science and Technology, (F) Science in Personal and Social Perspectives, and (G) History and Nature of Science.

This book will help teachers, students, parents, and tutors. Teachers can use this book either to introduce or review a topic in their science classroom. Students will find the book useful in reviewing the major concepts in science. Parents can use this book to help their children with topics that may be posing a problem in the classroom. Tutors can use this book as a basis for their lessons and for assigning questions and activities.

This book includes ten lessons that focus on the ten major concepts presented in the content standards: Physical Science, Life Science, and Earth and Space Science. The lessons also cover the twelve major concepts presented in the other standards. A table on page 4 provides a correlation between the contents of each lesson and the National Science Education Standards.

Before beginning the book, the reader can check his or her knowledge of the content by completing the *Assessment*. The *Assessment* consists of questions that deal with the content standards. This will allow the reader to determine how much he or she knows about a particular concept before beginning to read about it. The *Assessment* may also serve as a way of leading the reader to a specific lesson that may be of special interest.

Each lesson follows the same sequence in presenting the material. A list of *Key Terms* is always provided at the beginning of each lesson. This list includes all the boldfaced terms and their definitions presented in the same order that they are introduced in the lesson. The reader can develop a sense of the lesson content by glancing through the *Key Terms*. Each lesson then provides background information about the concept. This information is divided into several sections. Each section is written so that the reader is not overwhelmed with details. Rather, the reader is guided through the concept in a logical sequence. Each lesson then moves on to a *Review*. This section consists of several multiple-choice and short-answer questions. The multiple-choice questions check if the reader has retained information that was covered in the lesson. The short-answer questions check if the reader can use information from the lesson to provide the answers.

Each lesson then moves on to a series of activities. These activities are designed to check the reader's understanding of the information. Some activities extend the lesson by presenting additional information. The activities are varied so as not to be boring. For example, reading passages about interesting and unusual findings are included. Questions to check reading comprehension are then asked. As a change of pace, some activities are meant to engage the reader in a "fun-type" exercise. These activities include crosswords, word searches, jumbled letters, and cryptograms.

The last activity in each lesson is an experiment. Each experiment has been designed so that the required items are easy to locate and can usually be found in most households. Care has been taken to avoid the use of any dangerous materials or chemicals. However, an adult should always be present when a student is conducting an experiment. In some cases, the experimental procedure reminds students that adult supervision is required. Before beginning any experiment, an adult should review the list of materials and the procedure. In this way, the adult will be aware of any situations that may need special attention. The adult should review the safety issues before the experiment is begun. The adult may want to check a laboratory manual for specific safety precautions that should be followed when doing an experiment, such as wearing safety goggles and never touching or tasting chemicals.

The book then follows with a *Science Fair* section. Information is presented on how to conduct and present a science fair project. In some cases, the experiment at the end of a lesson can serve as the basis for a science fair project. Additional suggestions are also provided with advice as to how to choose an award-winning science fair project.

A *Glossary* is next. This section lists all the boldfaced terms in alphabetical order and indicates the page on which the term is used. The book concludes with an *Answer Key*, which gives the answers to all the activity questions, including the experiment.

This book has been designed and written so that teachers, students, parents, and tutors will find it easy to use and follow. Most importantly, students will benefit from this book by achieving at a higher level in class and on standardized tests.

National Science Education Standards

Standard A: SCIENCE AS INQUIRY
A1 Abilities necessary to do scientific inquiry
A2 Understandings about scientific inquiry

Standard B: PHYSICAL SCIENCE
B1 Properties and changes of properties in matter
B2 Motions and forces
B3 Transfer of energy

Standard C: LIFE SCIENCE
C1 Structure and function in living things
C2 Reproduction and heredity
C3 Regulation and behavior
C4 Populations and ecosystems
C5 Diversity and adaptations of organisms

Standard D: EARTH AND SPACE SCIENCE
D1 Earth's history and structure
D2 Earth in the solar system

Standard E: SCIENCE AND TECHNOLOGY
E1 Abilities of technological design
E2 Understandings about science and technology

Standard F: SCIENCE IN PERSONAL AND SOCIAL PERSPECTIVES
F1 Personal health
F2 Populations, resources, and environments
F3 Natural hazards
F4 Risks and benefits
F5 Science and technology in society

Standard G: HISTORY AND NATURE OF SCIENCE
G1 Science as a human endeavor
G2 Nature of science
G3 History of science

Correlation to National Science Education Standards

Assessment

Darken the circle by the best answer.

Lesson 1

1. The temperature at which a gas turns into a liquid is called its

- (A) melting point.
- (B) freezing point.
- (C) boiling point.
- (D) condensation point.

2. In which state of matter are the particles farthest apart?

- (A) solid
- (B) liquid
- (C) gas
- (D) both solid and liquid

Lesson 2

3. Which force can cause an object to move?

- (A) balanced force
- (B) friction
- (C) air resistance
- (D) gravity

Lesson 3

4. Work is defined as

- (A) mass times energy.
- (B) force times distance.
- (C) energy released.
- (D) increase in temperature.

5. The energy an object has because of its motion is called

- (A) kinetic energy.
- (B) potential energy.
- (C) heat energy.
- (D) chemical energy.

Lesson 4

6. Which structure is found in only plant cells?

- (A) nucleus
- (B) cell wall
- (C) cell membrane
- (D) cytoplasm

7. During photosynthesis, plants

- (A) change sugars into carbon dioxide.
- (B) use oxygen.
- (C) produce sugars.
- (D) use water for energy.

Lesson 5

8. Which structure contains a tiny, undeveloped plant?

- (A) pistil
- (B) stigma
- (C) anther
- (D) seed

Assessment, page 2

Lesson 6

9. Learned behavior is determined by

Ⓐ experiences.

Ⓑ genes.

Ⓒ heredity.

Ⓓ weather.

10. Which of the following is not involved when you jump after hearing a loud noise?

Ⓐ stimulus

Ⓑ brain

Ⓒ response

Ⓓ spinal cord

Lesson 7

11. Which diagram illustrates an herbivore eating a producer?

Ⓐ seeds → mouse

Ⓑ deer → mountain lion

Ⓒ prairie dog → coyote

Ⓓ dead remains → vulture

12. All the living and nonliving things in an environment make up a(n)

Ⓐ energy pyramid.

Ⓑ food chain.

Ⓒ food web.

Ⓓ ecosystem.

Lesson 8

13. Which classification group represents the highest level?

Ⓐ kingdom

Ⓑ species

Ⓒ family

Ⓓ genus

Lesson 9

14. Which layer of Earth is closest to the surface?

Ⓐ mantle

Ⓑ lithosphere

Ⓒ crust

Ⓓ core

15. Which layer of the atmosphere is farthest from Earth?

Ⓐ thermosphere

Ⓑ mesosphere

Ⓒ stratosphere

Ⓓ troposphere

Lesson 10

16. From which structure did the planets develop?

Ⓐ the sun

Ⓑ asteroids

Ⓒ the solar nebula

Ⓓ comets

Assessment
Science 5, SV 9781419034336

Lesson 1 Properties and Changes of Properties in Matter

You know that if you placed an ice cube in a glass, it would slowly melt. Eventually, only water would be left in the glass. If you left the water in the glass, it would slowly evaporate. Eventually, there would be nothing left in the glass. The ice cube was a solid. The ice cube melted to form water, which is a liquid. The liquid then evaporated to form a gas, which rose and spread out into the air. Therefore, a solid changed into a liquid, which then changed into a gas. In this lesson, you will learn more about solids, liquids, and gases.

States of Matter

Solids, liquids, and gases are three states of matter. A **state of matter** is the physical form in which a substance can exist. For example, water commonly exists in three states of matter: solid (ice), liquid (water), and gas (steam). But what is matter?

Key Terms

state of matter—the physical form in which a substance can exist

matter—anything that has both volume and mass

volume—the amount of space taken up, or occupied, by an object

mass—the amount of matter in an object

weight—a measure of the force of gravity on the mass of an object

solid—the state of matter that has a definite shape and a definite volume

atom—the building block of matter

liquid—the state of matter that has a definite volume but takes the shape of its container

surface tension—a force that holds together the particles of a liquid at its surface

gas—the state of matter that has no definite shape or definite volume

change of state—the change of a substance from one physical form to another

energy—the ability to do work

melting point—the temperature at which a solid turns into a liquid

freezing point—the temperature at which a liquid turns into a solid

boiling point—the temperature at which a liquid turns into a gas

condensation—the change of state from a gas to a liquid

condensation point—the temperature at which a gas turns into a liquid

Matter is anything that has both volume and mass. **Volume** is the amount of space that is taken up, or occupied, by an object. The volume of an ice cube is the amount of space it takes up in a glass of iced tea. **Mass** is the amount of matter in an object. The mass of an object is often thought of as its weight. However, mass and weight are not the same. **Weight** is a measure of the force of gravity on the mass of an object.

The mass of an object is always the same no matter where the object is located in the universe. In contrast, the weight of an object depends on where the object is located. For example, an astronaut will weigh much less on the moon where the force of gravity is much less than it is on Earth. However, the astronaut has the same mass both on the moon and on Earth.

Matter is made up of tiny particles that are too small to see without the help of a very powerful microscope. If you could see these particles, you would notice that they are always moving and bumping into one another. However, the particles move differently in a solid, liquid, and gas. In fact, the way the particles move determines the state of matter.

Solids

Suppose that you are holding a small magnet in the palm of your hand. What would happen to the shape and size of the magnet if you dropped it into a glass? Its shape and size would not change. The shape and size of the magnet would not change no matter where you placed it.

The shape and size of the magnet do not change because it is a solid. A **solid** is the state of matter that has a definite shape and a definite volume. The particles that make up a solid are very close to one another.

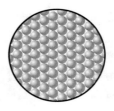

Notice that particles in a solid are so close that they touch one another. Each particle in a solid is locked in place by the particles that surround it. As a result, the particles in a solid can move, but they cannot move out of place. Instead, the particles move, or vibrate, in place. This means that the particles in a solid stay in place, moving back and forth like the strings on a guitar.

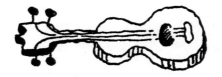

Although the particles are very close to one another, they are not arranged the same way in all solids. For example, consider two very different solids: diamond and graphite. Diamond is a very expensive substance that is used to make jewelry. Diamond is also the hardest substance known. Because of its hardness, diamond is used to make cutting tools, such as saws and drills. Graphite is an inexpensive substance that is used as pencil "lead." Graphite is a very soft substance that crumbles easily on paper as you write with a pencil.

Despite their differences, both diamond and graphite are made of exactly the same particles. These particles are carbon atoms. An **atom** is the building block of all matter. The carbon atoms in both diamond and graphite are very close to one another, making both substances a solid. However, the carbon atoms are arranged very differently in diamond and graphite.

In diamond, the carbon atoms are packed very closely together as a single unit. Each carbon atom is connected to other carbon atoms. As a result, all the carbon atoms are held tightly to one another, making diamond very hard.

In graphite, the carbon atoms do not form a single unit. Rather, they form separate layers. The carbon atoms in each layer are connected to one another. However, the carbon atoms in one layer are not connected to the carbon atoms in another layer. As a result, the layers can slide past one another. As you write with a pencil, the graphite

layers slide past one another. This leaves a trail of graphite on the paper.

Liquids

Suppose that you pour a glass of milk. Now suppose that you pour the milk from the glass into a larger glass. You would still have the same volume of milk. The only thing that would change is the shape of the milk. The shape changes because milk is a liquid. A **liquid** is the state of matter that has a definite volume but takes the shape of its container.

The particles that make up a liquid move more quickly than those in a solid. In fact, the particles in a liquid move fast enough so that they can slide past one another. They slide past one another until the liquid takes the shape of its container.

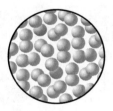

Liquids have an unusual property at their surface. This property is called surface tension. **Surface tension** is a force that holds together the particles of a liquid at its surface. This force can be strong enough so that the particles at the surface can support a lightweight object, such as a paper clip. Surface tension depends on the particles that make up the liquid. For example, the particles of water are more strongly attracted to one another than the particles of gasoline. Therefore, the surface tension of water is much higher than the surface tension of gasoline.

Gases

Suppose that you blow up a balloon. Then suppose that you allow the air to escape. The balloon deflates as the air inside escapes into the room. Air is a mixture of gases. A **gas** is the state of matter that has no definite shape or volume. A gas takes the shape and volume of its container. The air that once had the shape and volume of the balloon took the shape and volume of the room as it escaped.

Gases have no definite shape or volume because their particles move very quickly. They move so quickly that they can break apart from one another. As the particles move father and farther apart, the empty spaces between them get larger and larger.

Because a gas takes the shape and volume of its container, one tank of helium gas can fill hundreds of balloons. The gas particles inside the tank are compressed or squeezed together. If the valve on the tank is opened, the gas particles quickly move apart and escape. They push against the elastic balloon, filling it with helium gas. The gas particles in the balloon are much farther apart than they were inside the tank. This is why one tank of helium gas can fill hundreds of balloons.

Changes in State: Melting and Freezing

When an ice cube melts, it goes through a change of state. A **change of state** is the change of a substance from one physical form to another. Examples of changes of state include a solid melting to form a liquid and a liquid freezing to form a solid.

All changes in state involve a change in energy. **Energy** is defined as the ability to do work. Energy exists in different forms. One form of energy is heat. When heat energy is added, a solid melts to form a liquid. Recall that the particles in a solid vibrate in place. When heat is added, these particles gain energy and therefore move faster. If they gain enough energy, the particles can move apart from one another. At this point, the solid begins to melt. The temperature at which a solid melts is called its **melting point**.

Not all solids have the same melting point. For example, gallium is a solid metal that melts at about 30°C. Therefore, gallium metal will melt in your hands because normal body temperature is about 37°C. In contrast, table salt melts at about 800°C. Therefore, table salt will not melt in your hands no matter how long you hold it.

If energy must be added to melt a solid, then energy must be removed to freeze a liquid. Removing energy from a liquid causes the particles to move more slowly. If enough energy is removed, then the particles will stop moving and just vibrate in place. At this point, the liquid freezes to become a solid. The temperature at which a liquid freezes is called its **freezing point**.

Changes in State: Boiling and Condensing

If heat is added to a liquid, the particles gain energy and move faster. If they gain enough energy, the particles can move far apart from one another. At this point, the liquid begins to boil and forms a gas. The temperature at which a liquid boils is called its **boiling point**.

Not all liquids have the same boiling points. The boiling point of water is 100°C. In contrast, the boiling point of liquid oxygen, which is used as a rocket fuel, is −183°C. Therefore, liquid oxygen would boil if it were left in an open container.

If energy must be added to change a liquid into a gas, then energy must be removed to change a gas into a liquid. The process of changing a gas into a liquid is called **condensation**. Removing energy from a gas causes the particles to move more slowly. If enough energy is removed, then the particles will move slowly enough so that they just slide past one another. At this point, the gas turns into a liquid. The temperature at which a gas becomes a liquid is called its **condensation point**.

Lesson 1, Properties and Changes of Properties in Matter
Science 5, SV 9781419034336

Lesson 1

Review

Darken the circle by the best answer.

1. The temperature at which a liquid turns into a solid is called its
   - Ⓐ melting point.
   - Ⓑ freezing point.
   - Ⓒ boiling point.
   - Ⓓ condensation point.

2. In which state of matter are the particles closest together?
   - Ⓐ solid
   - Ⓑ liquid
   - Ⓒ gas
   - Ⓓ both liquid and gas

3. As a solid turns into a liquid, the particles
   - Ⓐ get closer together.
   - Ⓑ have less energy.
   - Ⓒ stop vibrating.
   - Ⓓ move farther apart from one another.

4. Which of the following applies to a gas?
   - Ⓐ definite shape and volume
   - Ⓑ definite volume but no definite shape
   - Ⓒ no definite shape or volume
   - Ⓓ definite shape but no definite volume

5. What must happen to the particles in a liquid for it to turn into a gas?
   - Ⓐ They must gain more energy.
   - Ⓑ They must release energy.
   - Ⓒ They must keep the same amount of energy.
   - Ⓓ They must move less quickly.

6. Surface tension is found in a
   - Ⓐ solid.
   - Ⓑ liquid.
   - Ⓒ gas.
   - Ⓓ gas that is condensing into a liquid.

7. Describe how the arrangement and motion of the particles in a substance change as a substance melts.

   _____

   _____

   _____

8. Explain why the particles of a liquid take the shape of its container.

   _____

   _____

   _____

   _____

   _____

Lesson 1   Models

Scientists often use models in their work. You have examined models that represent solids, liquids, and gases in this lesson. Examine the following models that show the arrangements of particles in different samples of matter.

model A

model B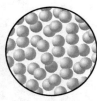

model C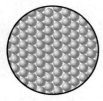

model D

1. Which model represents a state of matter that has a definite volume but not a definite shape? Explain the reason for your choice.

   _____

   _____

2. Which model(s) represent a state of matter where the particles have the highest amount of energy? Explain the reason for your choice(s).

   _____

   _____

3. What will happen to the volume and shape of the state of matter represented by model C when it is placed in containers with different volumes and shapes?

   _____

   _____

4. Which models represent states of matter that are present at the boiling point of a substance? Explain the reason for your choices.

   _____

   _____

Lesson 1, Models
Science 5, SV 9781419034336

Lesson 1   Solids, Liquids, and Gases

Find the words that complete the following sentences in the word search puzzle. The words may appear horizontally, vertically, or diagonally. All the words are listed in the *Key Terms* on page 7.

1. At the condensation point, a _____ turns into a _____.

2. The particles in a _____ vibrate but do not move apart.

3. A liquid turns into a solid at the _____ point.

4. _____ is needed to move apart the particles in a liquid to turn it into a gas.

5. An unusual property of liquids is their _____.

6. _____ are the building blocks of solids, liquids, and gases.

7. Both solids and liquids have a definite _____.

```
W  C  B  N  D  S  R  F  I  W  E  E  D  Q  S
E  T  F  Z  M  I  O  Q  N  R  M  B  V  L  U
R  U  L  O  E  X  U  E  H  Y  U  X  S  N  R
W  O  T  N  R  V  P  Q  V  Z  L  T  Q  V  F
Y  A  X  I  Q  X  J  F  I  E  O  Q  G  N  A
S  O  L  I  D  S  R  L  U  L  V  Z  B  J  C
H  C  G  F  T  E  X  L  I  Y  G  R  E  N  E
U  B  N  V  E  N  L  X  E  D  T  S  X  R  T
G  A  P  Z  V  D  L  H  H  U  Z  T  A  I  E
B  G  I  M  F  U  W  Q  A  Y  C  G  U  X  N
K  N  A  V  S  S  X  A  F  C  F  T  E  W  S
G  E  L  S  Z  C  N  K  C  W  F  V  Q  B  I
N  Q  K  P  T  A  V  X  U  N  C  B  M  X  O
S  L  D  C  Z  Z  L  J  T  J  K  K  Y  X  N
V  L  L  Z  J  W  G  N  Y  Q  Y  A  C  N  F
```

Lesson 1   Hot Air Balloons

Read the following passage. Then answer the questions that follow the passage.

Have you ever seen a hot air balloon floating through the air? If not, then perhaps you have seen pictures of one. These flying machines have no engines or steering devices. A hot air balloon consists of three basic parts: a basket to carry passengers, a balloon to hold the air, and burners to heat the air. Hot air balloons burn propane, the same gas that is used in outdoor barbecues.

Hot air balloons were made possible because of a discovery made by a French scientist named Jacques Charles (1746–1823). In addition to his interest in science, Charles loved to fly in balloons that were very popular at the time. These balloons were filled with hydrogen gas. Because hydrogen is lighter than air, a balloon filled with this gas can float through the sky. However, hydrogen gas is very explosive. Charles realized that another, safer method was needed.

Charles conducted experiments on gases. He discovered that increasing the temperature increased the volume of a gas. In other words, the warmer a gas gets, the more it expands. Charles's experiments led to a law that explains the relationship between the volume of a gas and its temperature. This became known as Charles's law. Today, hot air balloons can float safely through the sky because of Charles's law.

1. Why are burners needed on a hot air balloon?

Ⓐ to steer the balloon

Ⓑ to keep the passengers warm

Ⓒ to heat the air

Ⓓ to burn propane for cooking

2. Hydrogen gas is dangerous to use because it

Ⓐ is lighter than air.

Ⓑ is explosive.

Ⓒ changes its volume when heated.

Ⓓ changes its shape when heated.

3. Charles's law shows how temperature affects the

Ⓐ kind of gas used to fill a hot air balloon.

Ⓑ mass of a gas.

Ⓒ condensation point of a gas.

Ⓓ volume of a gas.

4. The warmer a gas gets,

Ⓐ the farther apart its particles spread.

Ⓑ the closer together its particles get.

Ⓒ the more explosive it becomes.

Ⓓ the more mass it has.

Lesson 1   Experiment: Freezing Water

You learned in this lesson that energy is needed to change the state of matter. For example, heat energy may be added to change a solid into a liquid. In contrast, heat energy may be removed to change a liquid into a solid. But does adding heat energy cause a substance's temperature to rise? Also, does removing heat energy cause a substance's temperature to drop? In this experiment, you will find the answers to these questions.

What You Will Need

baby food jar
large coffee can
ice cubes
rock salt
thermometer
watch or clock

Procedure

1. Fill the baby food jar about one-half full with water.

2. Put the jar in the coffee can. Fill in around the jar with ice cubes. Pour rock salt on the ice cubes.

3. Place the thermometer in the jar.

4. Record the temperature of the water every minute.

5. Gently stir the water with the thermometer after each reading.

6. Add ice cubes and rock salt to the coffee can to keep the water in the jar surrounded by the ice-salt mixture.

7. Once the water begins to freeze, stop stirring.

8. Notice the temperature when ice first appears inside the jar.

9. Continue recording the temperature until the water in the jar is completely frozen.

10. Remove the jar, allow the ice to melt, and then remove the thermometer.

Experiment: Freezing Water (cont'd.)

Results and Analysis

Describe the changes in the temperature of the water as heat energy is removed through cooling.

_____

_____

_____

Conclusion

Based on your results, what conclusion can you draw about the temperature of a substance as it changes its state, for example from a liquid to a solid?

_____

_____

Lesson 2 Motions and Forces

Look around and you will probably see something moving. Perhaps your dog is walking across the room. Or a car is driving past your house. There are also things moving that you cannot see. For example, the air around you is constantly moving. The ground you are standing on is moving as Earth orbits the sun. In this lesson, you will learn more about motion and what causes an object to move.

Motion

Suppose that you are in a car traveling at 50 miles per hour along a highway. Also suppose that another car is traveling at 50 miles per hour in the lane next to your car. If you look just at the people in the other car, the car will not seem to be moving at all, even though it is traveling at 50 miles per hour. However, if you look at the tires on the other car and the road, you can definitely tell that the car is moving.

In order to tell if an object is moving, you need a reference point. A reference point is the object that appears to stay in place in relation to another object that is moving. In this case, the road is a reference point. By looking at the tires and the road, you can tell that the other car is in motion. **Motion** occurs when an object changes position over time with respect to a reference point.

Earth is the most commonly used reference point. For example, if you are flying in an airplane, you may not be able to tell that you are moving unless you look down at the ground. Recall, however, that Earth is always moving. Therefore, a reference point, such as Earth, does not really stay in place. Reference points are also in motion. It's just that a reference point is not moving at the same speed or in the same direction as the object in motion.

Key Terms

motion—the change in position of an object over time with respect to a reference point

speed—the distance traveled by an object divided by the time it takes to travel that distance

velocity—the speed of an object in a particular direction

acceleration—the rate at which velocity changes

force—a push or pull on an object

gravity—a force of attraction between two objects

newton—the unit for force

friction—a force that opposes motion between two surfaces that are in contact

Speed

The cars mentioned earlier were traveling at 50 miles per hour. This is their speed. **Speed** is the distance traveled by an object divided by the time it takes to travel that distance. For example, these cars travel a distance of 50 miles in 1 hour. Speed can be expressed in various units in addition to miles per hour (mi/h). These units include feet per second (f/s), and, in the metric system, meters per second (m/s) and kilometers per hour (km/h).

Suppose you walk 2 miles in 1 hour. Your speed would be 2 mi/h. However, during your walk, you may stop to tie your shoelaces. Or you may walk faster because you see something. In any case, you would not walk at a constant speed of 2 mi/h but rather slower at some times and faster at other times. Therefore, your speed is actually an average speed. The following equation is used to calculate the average speed.

$$\text{average speed} = \frac{\text{total distance}}{\text{total time}}$$

$$\text{average speed} = \frac{2 \text{ mi}}{1 \text{ h}}$$

Velocity

Speed indicates the distance an object moves and how long it takes to move that distance. However, speed does not indicate in which direction the object is moving. For example, you know the speeds of the cars mentioned earlier—50 mi/h. However, you do not know whether they are traveling north, east, south, or west.

Knowing their direction can be very important. If the cars are traveling in the same direction, then they will wind up in the same place after one hour. However, if the cars are traveling in opposite directions, they then will wind up 100 miles apart after one hour. Even though the two cars are traveling in opposite directions, they have the same average speed. However, the two cars have different velocities.

Velocity is the speed of an object in a particular direction. The velocity of one car may be 50 mi/h south. The velocity of the other car may be 50 mi/h north. Notice that velocity must include both speed and direction.

If the speed of a moving object changes, then its velocity also changes. If a car traveling at 50 mi/h speeds up to 55 mi/h, then its velocity changes. If the direction of a moving object changes, then its velocity also changes. If a car maintains its speed at 50 mi/h but turns to move into another lane, then its velocity also changes. Notice that velocity can change even if the speed remains constant.

Acceleration

All cars have an accelerator pedal. Pressing down on the accelerator makes a car go faster. To most people, the word *accelerate* means to "speed up" or "move faster." However, acceleration has a different meaning in science. **Acceleration** is the rate at which velocity changes.

For example, a car may go from 50 mi/h to 55 mi/h. As a result, its speed increases. Its velocity also increases because its speed increases. Its acceleration also increases because its velocity increases.

You learned that the velocity changes if either the speed or the direction of a moving object changes. Therefore, acceleration also changes if either the speed or the direction of a moving object changes. A car moving at 50 mi/h may turn to change lanes. The car's speed remains the same. However, the car's velocity changes because it changes direction. The car's acceleration changes because its velocity changes.

The following table illustrates the difference between speed, velocity, and acceleration.

Forces

In science, a **force** is simply a push or pull. Force is needed to set an object in motion. Force is also needed to change the motion of an object. Finally, force is needed to stop an object in motion.

Just because a force is acting on an object does not mean the object will start to move, change its motion, or stop. For example, consider two teams playing a tug-of-war contest. Each team is pulling on the rope in opposite directions. If both teams pull with the same force, the rope will not move. In this case, the two forces are balanced. *Balanced forces* do not cause an object to start moving, change its motion, or cause it to stop moving.

If one team pulls with more force, then the rope will move. In this case, the two forces are unbalanced because one force is greater than the other. *Unbalanced forces* cause an object to start moving, change the motion of an object, or cause it to stop moving.

	Car goes from 50 mi/h south to 55 mi/h south	Car going 50 mi/h south turns west	Car goes from 50 mi/h south to 45 mi/h south
Speed	Increases	Remains the same	Decreases
Velocity	Increases	Changes	Decreases
Acceleration	Increases	Changes	Decreases

Gravity

The force exerted by pulling on a rope is easy to see. However, not all forces can be seen. One force that cannot be seen is gravity. **Gravity** is a force of attraction between two objects. The force of gravity can cause an object to start moving. Gravity can also affect the motion of an object by changing its speed, velocity, or acceleration.

You are probably familiar with Earth's gravity that keeps everything from flying up into the air. Earth's force of gravity is very large. This force of gravity pulls everything toward the center of Earth. Another force is always needed to overcome Earth's force of gravity. In some cases, the force that is needed is very large. For example, a very large force is needed so that a rocket can lift off from Earth and overcome its gravity.

The force of Earth's gravity on an object is measured as the object's weight. The unit of weight you are familiar with is the pound (lb). However, scientists use a different unit when dealing with forces. The unit they use for force is called a **newton** (N). This unit is named after a British scientist named Isaac Newton (1642–1727). Newton was the first scientist to explain how gravity affects the motion of objects.

The force of gravity depends on an object's mass. You learned in Lesson 1 that mass is the amount of matter that an object contains. Our moon has a mass than is one-sixth that of Earth. Therefore, the force of gravity on the moon is one-sixth the force

of gravity on Earth. On Earth, a 100-lb person actually weighs about 445 N. On the moon, the same person would weigh about 75 N (445 N/6). That person, however, still has the same mass, whether he or she is on the moon or Earth.

Gravity is an example of a *noncontact* force. A noncontact force exists between two objects that are not touching one another. Other examples of noncontact forces include electrical forces and magnetic forces. Electrical forces cause your hairs to stand up when you hold a comb near your head on a cold day. Magnetic forces hold small magnets to a refrigerator door.

Friction

You know that a ball that is rolling will eventually stop. You learned that a force is needed to stop an object in motion. Friction is the force that stops the rolling ball. **Friction** is a force that opposes motion between two surfaces that are in contact. Notice that the two surfaces must be in contact for friction to operate. Therefore, friction is an example of a *contact force*.

Other contact forces include buoyancy and tension. Buoyancy is the force that allows objects, such as ships or swimmers, to float on water. Tension is a force that pulls or stretches something, such as a rope pulling a sled.

The following table summarizes the various types of forces.

Noncontact Forces	Contact Forces
Gravity	Friction
Electricity	Buoyancy
Magnetism	Tension

Lesson 2

Review

Darken the circle for the best answer.

1. Which of the following is a contact force?

Ⓐ gravity

Ⓑ magnetic force

Ⓒ friction

Ⓓ electrical force

2. Which force holds a picture on a wall?

Ⓐ electrical force

Ⓑ magnetic force

Ⓒ friction

Ⓓ tension

3. An object can start to move only when the force applied to it is

Ⓐ balanced.

Ⓑ unbalanced.

Ⓒ coming from opposite directions.

Ⓓ gravity.

4. What two factors must be known to calculate the speed of an object in motion?

Ⓐ direction and type of force being applied

Ⓑ distance and direction

Ⓒ distance and type of force being applied

Ⓓ distance and time

5. Which of the following is a noncontact force?

Ⓐ gravity

Ⓑ tension

Ⓒ friction

Ⓓ buoyancy

6. What two factors indicate the velocity of an object in motion?

Ⓐ speed and distance

Ⓑ speed and time

Ⓒ speed and direction

Ⓓ direction and time

7. What is needed to determine if an object is in motion?

Ⓐ friction

Ⓑ the object's mass

Ⓒ a reference point

Ⓓ balanced forces

8. Calculate the average speed of a plane that flies 1200 miles in 3 hours.

Review (cont'd.)

9. A bicycle rider is moving at a constant speed of 15 mi/h. How is it possible for her velocity to change if her speed does not change?

_____

_____

10. Two people are pushing on a box from opposite directions with the same amount of force. Will the box move? Explain the reason for your answer.

_____

_____

Lesson 2   Motions and Forces

Write the letter of the word or words on the right in front of the appropriate definition or description on the left. A letter may be used more than once. Item 10 has four lettered answers.

_____ **1.** unit for force	**a.** friction
_____ **2.** change in velocity	**b.** velocity
_____ **3.** push or pull	**c.** unbalanced forces
_____ **4.** one factor needed to calculate speed	**d.** newton
_____ **5.** noncontact force	**e.** acceleration
_____ **6.** speed in a particular direction	**f.** time
_____ **7.** invisible force	**g.** force
_____ **8.** contact force	**h.** distance
_____ **9.** another factor needed to calculate speed	**i.** gravity
_____ **10.** causes change in motion	

Lesson 2

Balanced and Unbalanced Forces

Read the following passage. Then answer the questions that follow the passage.

Designing a bridge involves calculating all the forces that will be acting on it. For example, the Golden Gate Bridge in San Francisco is a suspension bridge that is subject to various forces. A suspension bridge is one in which the roadway is hung, or suspended, from huge cables that extend from one end of the bridge to the other. The mass of the roadway is a large force that pulls down on these huge cables. Smaller cables that support the roadway also pull down on the main cables. In addition, the traffic that crosses the bridge creates another downward force on these cables. These huge cables must also withstand the force of the wind.

All these forces acting on the huge cables must be balanced. If not, the bridge would collapse. A suspension bridge is supported by towers. In the case of the Golden Gate Bridge, two towers that are 745 feet high (about the height of an 80-story building) push up on the main cables. The two towers balance all the forces that would otherwise cause the Golden Gate Bridge to collapse.

1. Which of the following statements is a fact from this passage?

Ⓐ The forces on this bridge are unbalanced.

Ⓑ The forces on this bridge are balanced.

Ⓒ Only upward forces act on this bridge.

Ⓓ Only downward forces act on this bridge.

2. Which structures provide the upward force on this bridge?

Ⓐ the roadways

Ⓑ the main cables

Ⓒ the smaller cables

Ⓓ the towers

3. What would happen if the downward forces were greater than the upward forces on this bridge?

Ⓐ More traffic could cross the bridge.

Ⓑ The two towers would not be needed.

Ⓒ The bridge would collapse.

Ⓓ The roadway could be made larger.

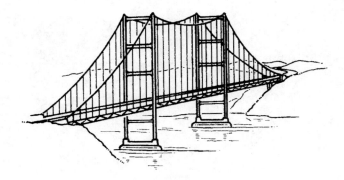

Lesson 2

Speed, Velocity, and Acceleration

Read the following problems and then answer the questions that follow.

Two buses filled with students left school at the end of the day. Both buses traveled at an average speed of 10 mi/h for 30 minutes.

1. How far did both buses travel?

_____

_____

2. How is it possible for the buses not to end up at the same place?

_____

_____

_____

A family from Virginia drove to California. The first day, they traveled 400 miles in 8 hours.

3. What was their average speed?

_____

_____

4. What was their velocity?

_____

_____

5. Explain how the acceleration of their car changed during the first day.

_____

_____

Lesson 2

Motions and Forces Crossword Puzzle

Across

4. speed of an object in a particular direction

6. change in position of an object over time

7. what forces must be to change the motion of an object

10. a contact force between two surfaces

Down

1. distance traveled divided by the time taken

2. force of attraction due to mass

3. change in velocity

5. a unit used for speed

8. unit for force

9. a push or pull

Lesson 2, Motions and Forces Crossword Puzzle
Science 5, SV 9781419034336

Lesson 2
Experiment: Detecting Acceleration

Have you ever been in a car that suddenly increased its speed or made a quick turn? If you have, then you may remember being pushed back against the seat when the car accelerated or being pushed toward one side when the car turned. In this experiment, you will build a device, called an accelerometer, that detects acceleration.

What You Will Need

string
scissors
1-liter plastic bottle with cap
tape
pushpin
cork that fits into bottle
water
tabletop with smooth surface

Procedure

1. Cut a piece of string that is about three-quarters the length of the bottle.

2. Use tape to attach one end of the string to the inside of the cap. Be sure the string is attached in the center of the cap.

3. Wrap the other end of the string around the pushpin. Insert the pushpin into the cork.

4. Fill the bottle with water.

5. Insert the cork and string into the bottle.

6. Put the lid on tightly.

7. Turn the bottle upside down on the table. The cork should float straight up in the water. This is your accelerometer.

8. Gently push the accelerometer across the table at a constant speed.

Experiment: Detecting Acceleration (cont'd.)

9. Describe what happens to the cork.

10. Experiment with your accelerometer by changing the speed and direction as you push it across the table.

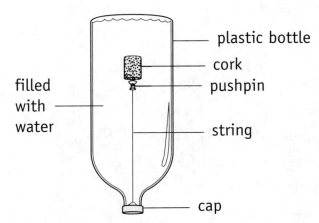

plastic bottle
cork
pushpin
filled
with
water
string
cap

Results and Analysis

1. What happens to the cork when you push the accelerometer across the table at a constant speed?

_____

_____

2. When does your accelerometer accelerate?

_____

_____

Conclusion

What conclusion can you draw from your results?

_____

_____

Lesson 3 Transfer of Energy

What did you do today? Perhaps you walked to school. Maybe you played with your friends. You may have ridden your bicycle. You might have gone shopping with your family. You may have even done your homework. Walking, playing, riding, shopping, and doing homework all require one thing. This is energy. The more energy you have, the more you can do. In Lesson 1, you learned that energy is the ability to do work. In this lesson, you will learn more about energy and where you can find it.

Energy and Work

You may think that you spend a lot of energy doing your homework. However, to a scientist, you would not have been doing much work at all. In science, **work** is done when a force causes an object to move in the direction of that force. The equation for work is written as follows.

$$\text{work} = \text{force} \times \text{distance or } W = F \times d$$

Notice that the object must move for work to be done. Suppose that you use 50 N of force to lift an object 1 meter (about 3 feet) off the ground. The amount of work you did is calculated as follows. Notice that the unit for work is the **joule**.

$$W = 50 \text{ N} \times 1 \text{ m} = 50 \text{ joules}$$

Key Terms

work—the use of a force that causes an object to move in the direction of the force

joule—the unit for work

kinetic energy—the energy an object has because of its motion

potential energy—the energy an object has because of its position

mechanical energy—the total energy of motion and position of an object

thermal energy—all the kinetic energy due to the random motion of the particles that make up an object

electron—an atomic particle that has a negative charge

electrical energy—the energy of moving electrons

light energy—the energy produced by the vibrations of electrically charged particles

sound energy—the energy produced by the vibrations of an object

chemical energy—the energy of a substance that changes as its atoms are rearranged

nuclear energy—the energy produced when matter is changed into energy

heat—the energy transferred between objects that are at different temperatures

energy conversion—the change of one form of energy to another

Simply applying force does not mean the work will be done. For example, no matter how much force you apply to a wall, the wall will never move. Because the wall is not set in motion, no work is being done. Even if an object is set in motion, this does not mean that work is being done.

For work to be done, the object must move in the direction of the force that is being applied. For example, you may get tired after carrying your backpack all day at school. However, you did not do any work to carry your backpack. The force you applied was in an *upward* direction to keep the backpack from falling to the ground. The backpack moved in a *forward* direction as you walked through the school.

Now suppose that a person is wearing a backpack and climbing up the side of a mountain. In this case, the person is doing work because the direction of motion and the force being applied are both upward. In fact, this person will do a lot of work.

Kinetic and Potential Energy

Suppose you are at a baseball game. The pitcher throws the ball. The batter is all set to swing at the ball. Both the ball and the bat have energy. The ball has kinetic energy. **Kinetic energy** is the energy an object has because of its motion. Kinetic energy depends on two factors.

One factor is mass. Suppose that a baseball and a tennis ball are moving through the air at the same velocity. Because the baseball has more mass, it has more kinetic energy than the tennis ball.

The other factor that affects kinetic energy is velocity. Suppose that a pitcher throws two balls. Both baseballs have the same mass. However, the pitcher throws the second ball with twice the velocity of the first ball. Because it has a greater velocity, the second ball has more kinetic energy than the first ball.

Think about the baseball game again. This time let's look at the batter. The bat has potential energy. **Potential energy** is the energy an object has because of its position. In this case, the bat has potential energy as the batter holds it in the air and gets ready to hit the ball. When the batter begins to swing the bat, its potential energy starts to change into kinetic energy. As the batter continues to swing, more potential energy is changed into kinetic energy as the bat moves faster. When the batter completes his swing, the bat's kinetic energy changes back to potential energy.

Therefore, an object can have all potential energy, all kinetic energy, or a combination of both. The total energy an object has is called mechanical energy. **Mechanical energy** is the total energy of motion and position of an object. The following equation shows the relationship between mechanical energy, kinetic energy, and potential energy.

mechanical energy = kinetic energy + potential energy

Thermal Energy

In addition to mechanical energy, there are other forms of energy. These forms of energy also involve kinetic and potential energy. An example is thermal energy. **Thermal energy** is all the kinetic energy due to the random motion of the particles that make up an object.

In Lesson 1, you learned about solids, liquids, and gases. You also learned how their particles are arranged. Because the particles in a solid vibrate in fixed positions, they do not have much kinetic energy. Therefore, the thermal energy of a solid is low. In contrast, the particles in a gas move very quickly. Therefore, they have more kinetic energy. As a result, a gas has more thermal energy than a solid.

Thermal energy is often measured as temperature. The temperature of water vapor (100°C) is higher than the temperature of ice (0°C). However, thermal energy also depends on the number of particles. As a result, an object with a lower temperature can have more thermal energy than an object with a higher temperature. For example, a pond has more thermal energy than a kettle of boiling water.

Electrical Energy

In Lesson 1, you learned that atoms are the building blocks of matter. Atoms consist of smaller particles. One of these particles is the electron. An **electron** is an atomic particle that has a negative charge. Electrons can move and therefore have kinetic energy. **Electrical energy** is the energy of moving electrons. The electrical energy used in your home provides the energy for your television, refrigerator, computer, radio, and many other devices.

Light Energy

The light from a lamp allows you to see. However, you cannot see all the light that exists. For example, a microwave oven uses light that you cannot see. An X-ray machine also uses light that you cannot see. All light, whether or not you can see it, is a form of energy. **Light energy** is produced by the vibrations of electrically charged particles.

Light energy can move through matter. For example, sunlight passes through a window. Light energy can also move through an area where there is no matter. This area is called a vacuum. In a vacuum, light energy travels at above 186,000 miles per hour. This is about the speed that light energy travels from the sun to Earth in the near vacuum of space.

Sound Energy

When an object vibrates, it transmits energy through the air around it. This is known as sound energy. **Sound energy** is produced by the vibrations of an object. For example, the strings on a guitar have potential energy. When they are struck, these strings vibrate. Therefore, their potential energy has been changed into kinetic energy. The vibrations of the strings transmit their kinetic energy as sound energy through the air. When this sound energy reaches your ears, you hear the music being played on the guitar.

Chemical Energy

Foods provide you with the energy you need. Foods contain chemical energy. **Chemical energy** is the energy of a substance that changes as its atoms are rearranged. For example, carbohydrates are one of the substances in foods. Digestion involves breaking down carbohydrates into smaller substances called sugars. Respiration then rearranges the atoms in sugar. Rearranging the atoms in sugar releases its chemical energy.

Nuclear Energy

In 1905, Albert Einstein published his famous equation $E = mc^2$. E represents energy. M represents mass. C represents the speed of light. This equation states that mass can be changed into energy, and that energy can be changed into mass. This equation also states that a very tiny amount of mass can be changed into an enormous amount of energy. This energy is known as nuclear energy. **Nuclear energy** is the energy produced when matter is changed into energy.

The energy given off by the sun comes from nuclear energy. In the sun, atoms fuse or join together. When atoms fuse, mass is changed into energy. Nuclear power plants also produce nuclear energy. In a power plant, atoms are split apart. When atoms split apart, mass is changed into energy. In both the sun and a nuclear power plant, a small amount of mass produces an enormous amount of energy.

Transfer of Energy

Have you ever wrapped your hands around a warm object on a cold day? This is one way to warm your hands. Your hands got warm because energy was transferred from the warm object to your cold hands. This energy was transferred as heat. **Heat** is the energy that is transferred between objects that are at different temperatures. Energy is always transferred as heat from the warmer object to the colder object until both objects have the same temperature.

Why does something, such as an ice cube, feel cold? In this case, you are touching something that has a lower temperature. Energy is transferred as heat from your hands to the ice cube. This transfer of heat from your hands happens quickly. As a result, your hands feel cold because they are losing energy as heat.

Conversion of Energy

You learned that potential energy can change into kinetic energy, and vice versa. This is an example of an energy conversion. An **energy conversion** is the change of one form of energy to another. Any form of energy can change into another. For example, electrical energy changes into light and sound energies when you turn on your television.

Lesson 3, Transfer of Energy
Science 5, SV 9781419034336

Lesson 3   Review

Darken the circle for the best answer.

1. What determines an object's thermal energy?
   - (A) its electrons
   - (B) the motion of its particles
   - (C) its potential energy
   - (D) the temperature

2. Mechanical energy is the sum of the
   - (A) light energy plus sound energy.
   - (B) nuclear energy plus chemical energy.
   - (C) kinetic energy plus heat.
   - (D) potential energy plus kinetic energy.

3. What two factors determine if work is being done?
   - (A) mass and energy
   - (B) potential and kinetic energy
   - (C) force and distance
   - (D) mass and force

4. Chemical energy is the energy stored in a substance such as sugar. Therefore, chemical energy is a form of
   - (A) potential energy.
   - (B) kinetic energy.
   - (C) thermal energy.
   - (D) mechanical energy.

5. Energy is always transferred as heat from a
   - (A) larger object to a smaller object.
   - (B) smaller object to a larger object.
   - (C) colder object to a warmer object.
   - (D) warmer object to a colder object.

6. Which form of energy is released when mass is changed into energy?
   - (A) light
   - (B) nuclear
   - (C) sound
   - (D) electrical

7. Describe what occurs when a radio is plugged into an outlet and turned on.

_____

_____

8. Describe what happens when a lamp is plugged into an outlet and turned on.

_____

_____

9. Work is done on a ball when a pitcher throws it. Is the pitcher still doing work on the ball as it travels toward the catcher? Explain your answer.

_____

_____

Lesson 3   Doing Work

You learned that work is done when a force causes an object to move in the direction of the force. The following illustration shows the forces and distances involved in the work done to get to the top of the hill. Notice that F_1 and d_1 represent work done when a hiker walks up a trail to reach the top of the hill. F_2 and d_2 represent the work done when a person climbs straight up the hill. Use this illustration to answer the questions that follow. Remember the formula to calculate the work done: $W = F \times d$.

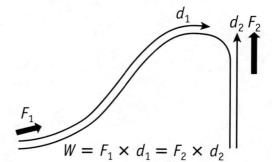

1. Which person travels the greater distance?

_____

2. Which person uses the greater force?

_____

3. How much work does the hiker do if he uses 800 N of force to walk 100 meters?

_____

4. How much work does the climber do if she uses 8000 N of force to climb 10 meters?

_____

5. Explain how it is possible for both the hiker and the climber to do the same amount of work even though they traveled different distances.

_____

_____

_____

Lesson 3

Juggling Energy

The following illustration shows a juggler tossing pins. Use this illustration to answer the questions that follow.

1. What kind of energy does a pin have as the juggler holds it? _____

2. What kind of energy does a pin have after the juggler tosses it? _____

3. What happens to the kinetic energy of a pin as it flies up in the air?

_____

_____

4. What happens to the potential energy of a pin as it starts to fall back down again?

_____

_____

5. What two types of energy change as a pin is juggled?

_____

6. What type of energy remains constant or the same as a pin is juggled?

_____

Lesson 3

Unscrambling Energy

Unscramble each of the following sets of letters to form a word found in the list of *Key Terms* **on page 30. Then use the circled letters to form the word that answers the question about energy.**

1. t e a h   __ ◯ __ __

2. n o s u d   __ __ __ ◯ __

3. g l i t h   ◯ __ __ __ __

4. l o j u e   __ __ ◯ __ __

5. m e h l a r t   __ __ __ ◯ __ ◯ __

6. n i c k e t i   __ __ __ __ __ __ ◯

What type of energy needs very little mass?

__ __ __ __ __ __ __ __

$$E = mc^2$$

Lesson 3   Experiment: Changing Energy

You learned that potential and kinetic energy can be changed into each other. The total energy known as mechanical energy, however, remains constant. In this experiment, you can see how much potential energy you can change into kinetic energy.

You Will Need

masking tape
12-foot section of clear plastic tubing
flat wall surface
small ball bearing that can roll easily through the tubing
stopwatch

Procedure

1. Tape the tubing to the wall to form a series of loops that go up and down. Make sure the beginning of the tubing is at the highest point on the wall.

2. Place the ball bearing inside the tubing at the highest point and release it.

3. If the ball bearing does not come out the other end, adjust the loops until it does. You may have to lower the height of some loops or you may have to decrease the number of loops that you have.

4. Time how long it takes for the ball bearing to complete its roller-coaster ride.

5. Experiment with your roller coaster by changing its design. Include a reverse loop.

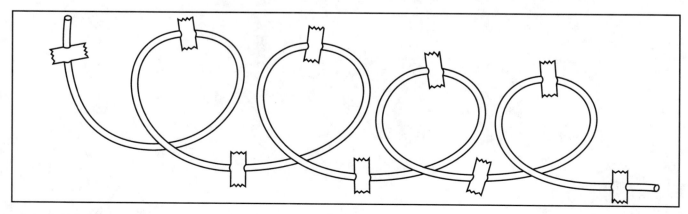

Experiment: Changing Energy (cont'd.)

Results and Analysis

1. Sketch the design that allowed the ball bearing to complete its ride in the shortest time.

2. When does the ball bearing have the most potential energy?

_____

Conclusion

What conclusion can you draw from your observations and results?

_____

_____

Lesson 4 Structure and Function in Living Things

Can you tell the difference between something that is living and something that is not living? In some cases, telling the difference is easy. For example, no one would have a problem telling that a dog is a living thing and that a rock is not a living thing. But what if you found something in the grass that was rather small, dark brown, and not moving? How could you tell if it was living? One way would be to use a microscope to take a close look at it. That is exactly what a scientist named Robert Hooke did.

The First Microscopes

In 1665, Hooke used a microscope he built to look at all sorts of things. His microscope was simple compared to the ones scientists use today. In fact, Hooke's microscope was even simpler than the one you use in school.

Key Terms

organism—a living thing

cell—the smallest unit that can perform all life processes

cell membrane—the protective layer that covers a cell's surface and controls what enters and leaves a cell

cytoplasm—the fluid and most of the structures inside a cell

nucleus—the cell structure that controls several functions, including reproduction

cell wall—a rigid structure that gives support to a plant cell

chloroplast—the structure where a plant cell makes food

photosynthesis—the process by which a plant cell makes food

chlorophyll—a green substance that traps sunlight for photosynthesis

eukaryotic cell—a cell that has a nucleus

prokaryotic cell—a cell that does not have a nucleus

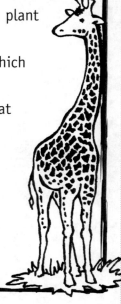

Hooke used his microscope to look at feathers, fish scales, the parts of plants, and even the eyes of houseflies. One day, he decided to take a closer look at a slice of cork. Cork comes from the bark of certain trees. Hooke used a sharp knife to make a very thin slice of cork. Looking through his microscope, Hooke saw that the cork looked like it was made of tiny little boxes.

What Hooke saw with his microscope reminded him of the tiny rooms where monks lived in a monastery. These rooms were called cells, which means "little rooms." Hooke became the first person to use the word *cell* in a scientific sense. He discovered that cork is not the only thing made of cells. Plants are also made of cells.

In 1673, Anton van Leeuwenhoek also used microscopes that he had built to look at all sorts of things. His microscopes were even simpler than Hooke's. Yet Leeuwenhoek was able to see an amazing variety of living things.

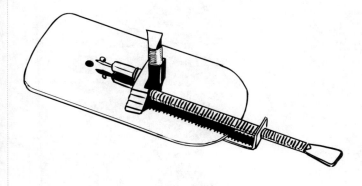

Leeuwenhoek discovered most of these living things, or **organisms**, in pond scum. Some of these organisms were bacteria. These organisms are so small that you might have trouble seeing them with a modern microscope. Despite his very simple microscope, Leeuwenhoek was able to describe and draw a variety of different bacteria.

About 150 years passed before another person would use the word *cell* in a scientific sense. In 1838, a scientist used a microscope to study plants. He concluded that all plants are made of cells. In 1839, another scientist concluded that all animals are made of cells. In 1859, still another scientist concluded that all cells can come only from other cells.

Cells and the Cell Theory

The work of all these scientists led to the development of the cell theory. This theory has three parts.

The Cell Theory
1. All organisms are made of one or more cells.
2. The cell is the basic unit of all living things.
3. All cells come only from other cells.

The first part states that all living things are made of cells. So, one way to tell if that tiny brown thing you found is living is to look for cells. You will learn more about what cells look like later in this lesson.

The second part of the cell theory states that the cell is the basic unit of an organism. A **cell** is defined as the smallest unit that can perform all life processes. So, that tiny brown thing must perform certain life processes if it is alive. You will learn about some of these life processes later in this unit.

The third part of the cell theory states that cells reproduce to form new cells. That tiny brown thing must have been produced by a cell if it is living. It must also be able to produce more like itself.

The Variety of Cells

Cells come in all shapes and sizes. Some cells are round, while others are long and thin. Most cells are too small to see without a microscope. For example, it would take 50 human skin cells to cover the dot on this letter *i*. However, some cells are quite large. A cell that is over six feet long stretches the length of a giraffe's neck.

The Structure of Cells

Although cells come in different sizes and shapes, they all share certain basic features. All cells are surrounded by a structure called a cell membrane. The **cell membrane** is a protective layer that covers the cell's surface. The cell membrane acts as a barrier. It separates the inside of a cell from its outside environment. The cell membrane controls what enters the cell from its environment.

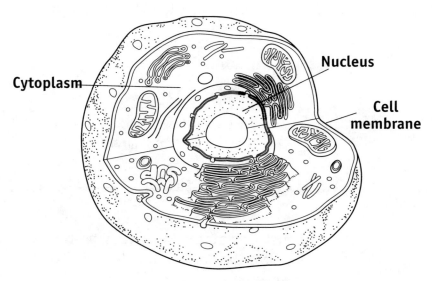

An Animal Cell

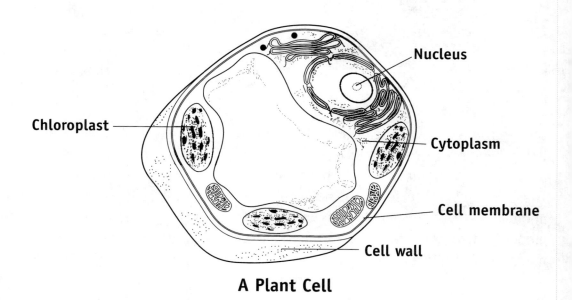

A Plant Cell

The cell membrane also controls what leaves the cell into its environment. Locate the cell membrane on each diagram.

Inside the cell is a fluid. This fluid contains various structures that the cell uses for different purposes. Together, the fluid and most of these structures make up the **cytoplasm**. Identify the cytoplasm in each diagram.

There is one structure inside most cells that is not part of the cytoplasm. This is the nucleus. The **nucleus** is a structure that is sometimes called the "control center" of the cell. This name is used because the nucleus contains the information that a cell uses to carry out many of its functions, including reproduction. Most of your cells have a nucleus. In contrast, bacterial cells do not have a nucleus. Find the nucleus in each diagram.

In humans, red blood cells do not have a nucleus. Red blood cells carry oxygen. Oxygen is needed by all the cells of your body. Cells use oxygen to get the energy they need. Without a nucleus, red blood cells have more room. Therefore, they can carry more oxygen. However, without a nucleus, red blood cells cannot survive very long. Human red blood cells survive between 100 to 120 days. Fortunately, red blood cells are constantly being made inside bones.

What Hooke saw in cork cells was actually a cell structure called a cell wall. A **cell wall** is a rigid structure that gives support to a plant cell. Plant cells are surrounded by a cell wall. The cell wall surrounds the cell membrane. Therefore, plant cells are surrounded by both a cell membrane and a cell wall. In contrast, animal cells are surrounded only by a cell membrane. Locate the cell wall in the plant cell diagram.

In some plants, the cell walls need water to keep their shape. If they do not have enough water, the cell walls lose their shape and collapse. The plant will begin to droop. If the plant obtains water, the cell walls will regain their shape. The plant will then stand upright.

Plant cells also contain another structure not found in animal cells. This is a chloroplast. A **chloroplast** is the structure where a plant cell makes food. Identify the chloroplasts in the plant cell diagram. Plants take in carbon dioxide and water. Plants use sunlight to change these two substances into sugar and oxygen. The process of making food in plants is called **photosynthesis**.

Chloroplasts contain a green substance called chlorophyll. **Chlorophyll** is responsible for the green color of most plants. Chlorophyll is also responsible for trapping the sunlight that the plant uses to make food.

The following table summarizes the structures of a cell.

Structure	Cell membrane	Nucleus	Cell wall	Chloroplast
Function	Controls what enters and leaves cell	Controls several cell functions	Provides support	Makes food
Animal cell	Present	Present	Absent	Absent
Plant cell	Present	Present	Present	Present

Types of Cells

There are two basic types of cells. One type of cell contains a nucleus. Cells that have a nucleus are called **eukaryotic cells**. Plant cells and animal cells are eukaryotic cells. A second type of cell does not contain a nucleus. Cells without a nucleus are called **prokaryotic cells**.

Prokaryotic cells also lack other structures that are found in eukaryotic cells. Because they lack a nucleus and other structures, prokaryotic cells are smaller and simpler than eukaryotic cells.

Prokaryotic cells include bacteria. Bacteria are the smallest cells in the world. Even though they are tiny, bacteria live almost everywhere. They live in the soil and water. They live inside other organisms, including you. Bacteria in your digestive system make vitamins that you need for good health. Many of the foods we eat are made with the help of bacteria. These foods include cheese, yogurt, and sour cream.

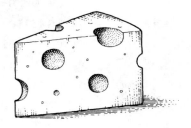

Humans cannot live without bacteria. However, certain bacteria can cause disease. For example, tetanus and diphtheria are two diseases caused by bacteria. Fortunately, most people today are protected against these diseases because they have been vaccinated. Diseases caused by bacteria can be treated with antibiotics.

www.harcourtschoolsupply.com
44
Lesson 4, Structure and Function in Living Things
Science 5, SV 9781419034336

Lesson 4 　　　　　　　　　　　Review

Darken the circle for the best answer.

1. Which of the following structures is found in all cells?
   - Ⓐ nucleus
   - Ⓑ cell wall
   - Ⓒ cell membrane
   - Ⓓ chloroplast

2. Which structure controls what enters and leaves a cell?
   - Ⓐ nucleus
   - Ⓑ cell membrane
   - Ⓒ cytoplasm
   - Ⓓ chloroplast

3. Which of the following statements is part of the cell theory?
   - Ⓐ All organisms are composed of one or more cells.
   - Ⓑ Most cells are too small to be seen without a microscope.
   - Ⓒ Cells exist in different shapes and sizes.
   - Ⓓ Bacteria are the simplest cells.

4. Which is the function of a cell wall?
   - Ⓐ traps light energy from the sun
   - Ⓑ controls what enters and leaves the cell
   - Ⓒ provides support
   - Ⓓ transports oxygen

5. During photosynthesis, plants
   - Ⓐ use oxygen.
   - Ⓑ produce oxygen.
   - Ⓒ produce carbon dioxide.
   - Ⓓ use sugars for energy.

6. When Robert Hooke used the word *cell* to describe what he saw through his microscope, which substance was he examining?
   - Ⓐ plants
   - Ⓑ blood
   - Ⓒ pond water
   - Ⓓ cork

7. In your own words, write a definition for the nucleus of a cell.

_____

_____

8. Explain why it took so long for scientists to develop the cell theory.

_____

_____

_____

Lesson 4   Cells I

Complete each of the following sentences by choosing the correct term from the following list of words. A term may be used more than once.

bacteria	chlorophyll
cell	cytoplasm
cell membrane	nucleus
cell wall	photosynthesis

1. A(n) _____ is found only in eukaryotic cells.

2. The basic unit of all living things is a(n) _____.

3. In plant cells, _____ traps sunlight to use in photosynthesis.

4. Both prokaryotic and eukaryotic cells are surrounded by a(n) _____.

5. Human red blood cells do not contain a(n) _____ so that they can carry more oxygen.

6. The fluid-filled inside of a cell is called the _____.

7. The process plant cells use to make food is called _____.

8. Prokaryotic cells include _____.

9. If a cell has a nucleus but it does not have a(n) _____, then it must be an animal cell.

10. A(n) _____ provides support and makes a cell rigid.

Lesson 4

Cells II

Find each of the eight terms from the list on the previous page in the following puzzle. They may appear horizontally, vertically, or diagonally. If you find all eight terms, you know your cells!

```
L H P D X M I A P X S F I P X J J S H T
X L J V W W I W K F S S H B C V P D U G
B S Y I Y R C J K A N O G A K I V H W F
L V F H E S W B J V T U V E F E O F T P
A R Z T P N Y C K O D P C D Q X G O K O
O Z C L C O K G S F B X T L D G P H A J
A A S Q G P R Y E N A R B M E M L L E C
B P N D J E N O J G N N C Q T U D E B J
N B X S F T C F L G T J E D S Q S H Q E
N U Q A H V E P E H P U C A F S E J V D
M X Y E R F L A A M C O S J P F T P H F
Q K S Q J A L T E S E P L D I D W Z V Z
Y I K V J N M J P A T H R U Z J I K S W
S F T U Q C U B U L Z I B H I E A X Z X
F O O N I R H Q J P T R O Q S U L H I V
C Y V M D L U F L O I Y Q R Z C C Q J J
F X A H A X B P H T Z P X W Z L W R X Z
C E L L W A L L L Y M W G Q J F J A D D
E E D F E S D M P C B V P T C E I W N D
B S U X C Z D X P M Y L A Z F O B X R X
```

Lesson 4, Cells II Science 5, SV 9781419034336

Lesson 4   Strange Creatures of the Deep

Read the following passage and then answer the questions.

Three people were huddled in a tiny vessel called the *Alvin*. The vessel was plunging deep into the Pacific Ocean. It sank for more than an hour until it finally reached the seafloor. The *Alvin* and its crew were more than 8000 feet below sea level. At this depth, the people aboard did not expect to see much life. But were they surprised.

One of the most amazing things they spotted was an organism called a giant tubeworm. Its name comes from the fact that its body is a long tube that stretches for almost 4 feet. One end of the tube is attached to the ocean floor, while the other end sways back and forth in the deep, dark water.

These tubeworms can survive in the deep ocean only with the help of bacteria. Without light, plants cannot survive near the ocean bottom. As a result, the bacteria are the only organisms that can make food in this environment. However, making food is no easy job. The tubeworms and bacteria live near openings in the ocean floor called thermal vents. Under high pressure, water pouring from these vents can reach temperatures up to 750°F. The high pressure keeps the water from boiling.

Each tubeworm has billions of bacteria living inside it. Scientists estimate that each ounce of tubeworm contains about 285 billion bacteria. All these bacteria make food for the tubeworm. In turn, the tubeworm provides shelter for the bacteria.

Other strange creatures living near thermal vents include shrimp that have no eyes and transparent crabs that are less than one-half inch in size.

1. What do all the creatures living near thermal vents have in common?
   - Ⓐ They make their own food.
   - Ⓑ They are small.
   - Ⓒ They are made of cells.
   - Ⓓ They cannot survive without sunlight.

2. Which organisms would be considered prokaryotic cells?
   - Ⓐ tubeworms
   - Ⓑ shrimp
   - Ⓒ crabs
   - Ⓓ bacteria

3. What is the main idea of this passage?
   - Ⓐ Organisms can survive in harsh environments.
   - Ⓑ Tubeworms can grow up to 4 feet long.
   - Ⓒ Plants are not the only organisms that can make food.
   - Ⓓ One tubeworm contains billions of bacteria.

NAME _____ DATE _____

Lesson 4   Experiment: Cell Size

Almost all cells are so small that you need a microscope to see them. Why don't cells get bigger? In this experiment, you will make models of cells. You will then do some measuring to see why cells would starve if they were too big.

You Will Need

ruler
pencil
thick piece of cardboard
scissors
tape
calculator

Procedure

1. Use the ruler to draw 6 squares on the cardboard. Each square should measure 1 inch on each side.

2. Cut out the 6 squares and tape them together to make a cube.

3. Repeat steps 1 and 2 but this time, draw each square on the cardboard so that it is 2 inches on each side.

4. Each cube represents a cell. The cardboard represents the cell membrane.

5. Calculate the volume, or space inside each cube, by multiplying S × S × S where S equals the length of one side. For example, the volume of the 1-inch cube equals 1 inch × 1 inch × 1 inch = 1 cubic inch.

6. Calculate the surface area, or the outer surface of each cube. This is done by multiplying S × S × 6. For example, the surface area of the 1-inch cube equals 1 inch × 1 inch × 6 = 6 square inches.

www.harcourtschoolsupply.com
© Harcourt Achieve Inc. All rights reserved.

49

Lesson 4, Experiment: Cell Size
Science 5, SV 9781419034336

Experiment: Cell Size (cont'd.)

Results and Analysis

1. Place your results in the following table.

Length of side	Volume	Surface Area
1 inch		
2 inches		

2. Find the ratio of the surface area to volume for each cube. For example, the surface area/volume ratio for the 1-inch cube equals 6/1. Place your results in the following table.

Length of side	Surface area/volume
1 inch	
2 inches	

3. Which cube has the larger surface area/volume ratio?

_____

Conclusions

1. What happens to the ratio of surface area to volume as a cube (cell) gets larger?

_____

_____

2. All the food a cell gets must pass through the outer surface of the cell membrane. Which is better able to supply food to all the cytoplasm of the cell—the cell membrane of a small cell or the cell membrane of a large cell? Explain the reason for your answer.

_____

_____

_____

Lesson 5 Reproduction and Heredity

All organisms reproduce, or make other organisms that are similar to themselves. In some cases, reproduction involves just one parent. The offspring that are produced are identical to this one parent. In other cases, two parents are involved in producing offspring. These offspring may share characteristics of both parents. For example, you may have heard someone say about a baby, "She has her mother's eyes and her father's mouth." In this lesson, you will learn two different ways that organisms reproduce.

Asexual Reproduction

In **asexual reproduction**, a single parent produces offspring that are identical to the parent. Most single-celled organisms, such as bacteria, reproduce asexually. There are several ways an organism can reproduce asexually. One way is called binary fission, which means splitting in two. **Binary fission** is a type of asexual reproduction in which

Key Terms

asexual reproduction—the process by which a single parent produces offspring that are identical to the parent

binary fission—a type of asexual reproduction in which one single-celled organism copies itself to form two single-celled organisms

DNA—the chemical substance that controls the structure and function of cells

budding—a type of asexual reproduction in which a part of the parent pinches off and forms a new organism

regeneration—a type of asexual reproduction in which a part of an organism breaks off and develops into a new individual

sexual reproduction—the process by which offspring are produced when the sex cells from two parents unite

sperm—the male sex cell

egg—the female sex cell

zygote—the cell produced when an egg and sperm unite

fertilization—the joining of an egg and sperm

stamen—the male reproductive structure of a flower

anther—the tip of a stamen

pollen—the tiny structures in which sperm form

pistil—the female reproductive structure of a flower

stigma—the tip of a pistil

one single-celled organism copies itself to form two single-celled organisms.

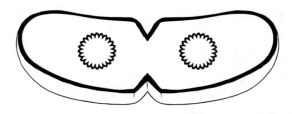

Like all organisms, bacteria contain information that is passed on to their offspring. This information is the blueprint that is needed for producing new cells. This blueprint is known as the hereditary information. The hereditary information is contained in a substance called deoxyribonucleic acid, or DNA. **DNA** controls the structure and function of cells.

The DNA in bacteria is found as circular loops, as you can see in the above illustration. Notice that before a bacterial cell splits in two, a copy is made of the DNA loops. As the bacterial cell grows, the DNA loops separate. The cell almost doubles its size. Notice that at this point, the cell membrane begins to pinch inward as shown in the above illustration. The cell membrane pinches inward to form two cells. Notice that each cell has one exact copy of the DNA that was in the parent cell. Because each cell has the identical DNA, both cells will be identical to each other and to their parent cell.

Budding

Another type of asexual reproduction is budding. **Budding** occurs when a part of the parent pinches off and forms a new organism. The new organism eventually separates from the parent. Although the new organism lives independently, it contains the identical DNA

as its parent. Therefore, budding produces an offspring that is identical to its parent. The following illustration shows how an organism known as a hydra reproduces asexually by budding.

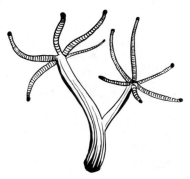

Regeneration

Sometimes an organism is broken into pieces or becomes fragmented. Perhaps the organism was carried by the current and smashed into a rock. Or the organism may have lost a part of its body when it was captured by another organism. If this happens, the organism may die.

However, some organisms can survive. In fact, the piece that is broken off can develop into a new individual. This is known as regeneration. **Regeneration** is a type of asexual reproduction where a part of an organism breaks off and then develops into a new organism. The following illustration shows a flatworm known as planaria that can reproduce by regeneration.

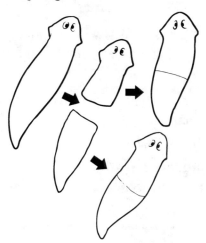

Plant Budding

Have you ever seen little buds growing on a potato? People call them the "eyes" of a potato. A potato is actually an underground stem that is called a *tuber*. The "eyes" are actual buds that can grow into new potato plants. Therefore, a potato can reproduce asexually by budding.

Other plants use different types of asexual reproduction. For example, strawberry plants produce stems that grow horizontally along the ground. These stems are called *runners*. Buds along the runners can take root and develop into new strawberry plants.

Some plants produce tiny plants along the edges of their leaves. These tiny plants are called *plantlets*. The plantlets eventually fall to the ground where they can root. A new plant can then develop from the plantlets.

Sexual Reproduction

Most animals reproduce sexually. In **sexual reproduction**, offspring are produced when the sex cells from two parents unite. The two parents include a male and a female. The sex cells produced by the male are called **sperm**. The sex cells produced by the female are called **eggs**. A sperm and an egg unite, or join, to form a single cell called a **zygote**. The joining of the sperm and egg is called **fertilization**.

Fertilization can occur either outside or inside a female's body. External fertilization occurs when a sperm fertilizes an egg outside a female's body. Many fishes and amphibians use external fertilization. A moist environment is needed so that the zygote will not dry out as it develops.

Internal fertilization occurs when a sperm fertilizes an egg inside a female's body. Internal fertilization provides an advantage because the chances of success are greater than those of external fertilization. Animals that use internal fertilization may then lay eggs that develop externally. For example, chickens lay one or two eggs that have been fertilized internally. In other animals that use internal fertilization, the zygote develops internally. Humans produce offspring as a result of internal fertilization and internal development.

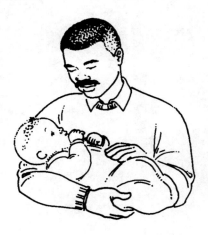

Flowering Plants

Do you have a favorite plant? Perhaps it is a rose plant that produces beautiful red flowers in summer. Or it may be an iris plant that has colorful purple flowers in spring. You may be fond of orchids because of their striking colors. For most people, their favorite plant is one that produces flowers. Flowering plants are the largest and most diverse group of plants. Their appeal and success is largely due to their flowers.

Plants carry out sexual reproduction with the help of their flowers. Flowers contain a male reproductive structure called the

stamen. At the tip of the stamen are tiny structures called **anthers**. The anthers contain **pollen**. Sperm form inside the pollen. Flowers also contain a female reproductive structure called a **pistil**. The tip of the pistil is called the **stigma**.

Insects and the wind transfer pollen from one plant to another plant. The pollen collects on the stigma, which are often sticky or feathery. Sperm from the pollen travel down the pistil to fertilize an egg. The fertilized egg develops into a seed. The seed contains a tiny, underdeveloped plant. Under the proper conditions, the seed can develop into an adult plant.

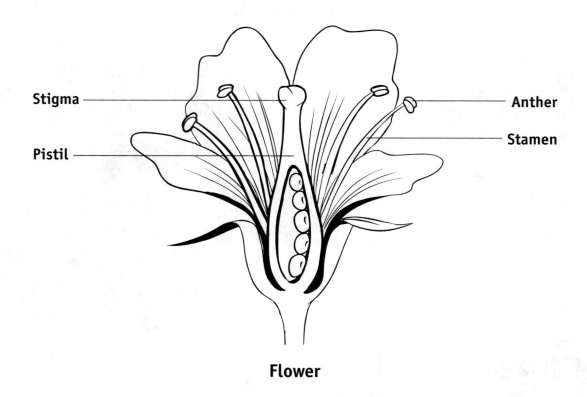

Stigma

Anther

Stamen

Pistil

Flower

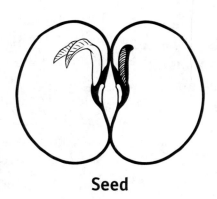

Seed

Lesson 5   Review

Darken the circle for the best answer.

1. Which is the name of the structure formed when fertilization occurs?
   Ⓐ sperm
   Ⓑ egg
   Ⓒ zygote
   Ⓓ pollen

2. Which type of asexual reproduction involves an individual developing from a piece of an organism?
   Ⓐ budding
   Ⓑ regeneration
   Ⓒ binary fission
   Ⓓ fertilization

3. How does sexual reproduction differ from asexual reproduction?
   Ⓐ Sexual reproduction involves only one parent.
   Ⓑ Sexual reproduction occurs only in animals.
   Ⓒ Sexual reproduction involves one organism splitting to form two offspring.
   Ⓓ Sexual reproduction involves two parents producing offspring.

4. The "eyes" that form on a potato are involved in
   Ⓐ asexual reproduction.
   Ⓑ sexual reproduction.
   Ⓒ fertilization.
   Ⓓ seed development.

5. Where are sperm formed in a plant?
   Ⓐ pistil
   Ⓑ stigma
   Ⓒ pollen
   Ⓓ seed

6. A part of a yeast cell pinches off and develops into another yeast cell. This is an example of
   Ⓐ binary fission.
   Ⓑ budding.
   Ⓒ regeneration.
   Ⓓ sexual reproduction.

7. How does internal fertilization differ from external fertilization?

   _____

   _____

8. Why is reproduction important for all organisms?

   _____

   _____

Lesson 5 — Unscrambling Reproduction

An anagram is a word or phrase formed by rearranging the letters of another word or phrase. For example, an anagram of the word *arm* would be *ram*. Notice that both the original term and the anagram contain the same letters, but they are arranged differently. Rearrange the following anagrams to create a single word that is related to reproduction.

1. SUE LAX _____

2. ALEX USA _____

3. ME STAN _____

4. HER TAN _____

5. DUD BING _____

6. IF SON IS _____

7. IN GREENER OAT _____

8. IF LATIN ZERO IT _____

Lesson 5   Twins

Sexual reproduction can sometimes produce twins. The twins can be either identical or fraternal. Identical twins have identical DNA or hereditary information. Fraternal twins do not contain identical DNA.

Examine the following diagram that shows how identical twins are produced.

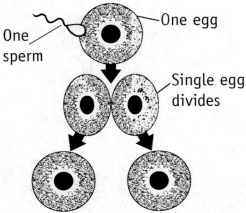

Examine the following diagram that shows how fraternal twins are produced.

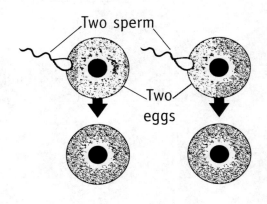

1. Explain why this diagram would produce identical twins.

   _____

   _____

   _____

2. Explain why fraternal twins can look very different from one another and can even be of opposite sexes.

   _____

   _____

   _____

Lesson 5   The Mathematics of Reproduction

1. On average, a woman produces one mature egg each month. A female starts producing an egg at about age 12. She stops producing an egg at about age 50. How many eggs will a woman produce from age 12 to age 50?

2. In the United States, identical twins happen about once in every 250 births. How many sets of identical twins might occur in 2000 births?

3. In the United States, there are about two sets of triplets produced in every 1000 births. How many sets of triplets might occur in 3000 births?

4. Puberty is the stage of life where a person's reproductive system becomes mature. Puberty usually begins between the ages of 11 and 16, and lasts about three years. Suppose a person is 80 years old. What percent of this person's life was spent in puberty?

Lesson 5

Experiment: A Model of Bacterial Reproduction

You learned that bacteria reproduce asexually by binary fission. If conditions are ideal, a bacterial cell can undergo binary fission every 20 minutes. Therefore, if you start with 1 cell, there will be 2 cells after 20 minutes, 4 cells after 40 minutes, and so on. In the following experiment, you will calculate and graph the numbers of bacteria that can be produced by binary fission.

You Will Need

calculator
pencil
paper
graph paper

Procedure

1. Assume that you start with 1 bacterial cell. Also, assume that these bacteria divide every 25 minutes. Use the calculator to determine how many bacteria will be present in 5 hours (300 minutes).

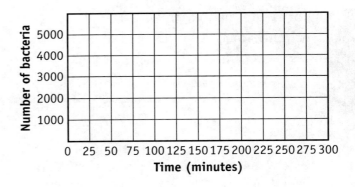

2. Plot the number of bacteria that are present after every 25 minutes on the graph.

Results and Analysis

How many bacteria can be produced in 5 hours from just 1 bacterial cell?

_____

Conclusion

What conclusion can you draw from your graph?

_____

UNIT 2 LIFE SCIENCE

Lesson 6 Regulation and Behavior

Have you ever been told to behave yourself? Perhaps you were talking to a friend in class while your teacher was speaking. You may have been reminded that talking in class when your teacher is talking is not considered acceptable behavior. Or you may have been going on a class field trip when your teacher reminded everyone to be on his or her best behavior. In this lesson, you will learn about behavior and the various ways animals behave.

Behavior

Behavior is the manner in which an organism acts. A **behavior** can be defined as an action or series of actions that an animal performs

in response to a stimulus. A **stimulus** is anything that causes a response. The stimulus for a particular behavior may be something in the organism's environment. For example, an animal might start running after hearing a loud noise.

The stimulus for a particular behavior may also be something that develops inside an organism. For example, your stomach may start "grumbling" because you are hungry. The "hunger pangs" you feel act as a stimulus that makes you behave by looking for something to eat.

Key Terms

behavior—an action or series of actions that an animal performs in response to a stimulus

stimulus—anything that causes a response

innate behavior—a manner of acting that does not depend on learning or experience

gene—a set of instructions that determines a trait an organism will have

hibernation—a period of decreased activity that some animals undergo during the winter

estivation—a period of decreased activity that some animals undergo during the summer

reflex—an innate behavior that involves an involuntary response to a stimulus

learned behavior—a behavior that has been learned from experience or by observing other organisms

conditioned behavior—a behavior that has been modified so that it occurs when another stimulus is substituted for the original stimulus

Innate Behavior

You are familiar with two kinds of behavior. One is acceptable behavior, and the other is unacceptable behavior. You know when someone is exhibiting acceptable behavior and when someone is exhibiting unacceptable behavior.

Scientists are also aware of different kinds of behavior. However, they do not classify behavior as either acceptable or unacceptable. Rather, one way they classify it is either as an innate behavior or as a learned behavior. **Innate behavior** is a manner of acting that does not depend on learning or experience. Innate behavior is inherited. You learned in the previous lesson that reproduction involves the passing of DNA from parents to offspring.

DNA carries the genes. A **gene** is a set of instructions that determines a trait an organism will have. The trait may be a physical feature such as the color of a person's eyes. The trait can also be a behavior that the organism displays. For example, an innate behavior in birds is the ability to fly. Another innate behavior in birds is nest building. Some birds will use colorful objects to build a nest in hope of attracting a female. Both flying and nest building are innate behaviors that birds inherit from their parents.

Hibernation

Most innate behaviors increase an organism's chances of survival. Hibernation is an example of such an innate behavior.

Hibernation is a period of decreased activity that some animals undergo during the winter to survive the freezing temperatures and lack of food. Animals that exhibit this behavior include mice, squirrels, and skunks. While in hibernation, an animal's temperature, heart rate, and breathing rate drop.

An example of an animal that hibernates is the arctic ground squirrel. This animal lives in an environment where temperatures can drop to −70°F. Winds that can blow up to 60 miles per hour can make it feel even colder. An arctic ground squirrel's heart normally beats about 200 times a minute. However, during hibernation this rate drops to about 10 beats per minute. During hibernation, the animal lives on the food it has stored in its body, usually as fat. Because its life processes have slowed down, the animal does not need as much food during hibernation.

The arctic ground squirrel is the only animal in that part of the world that truly hibernates in winter. Other animals slow down their life processes but do not enter hibernation. For example, bears sleep during the winter. However, they do not hibernate as their body temperature does not drop to just above freezing. A bear's heartbeat does not drop nearly as much as that of the arctic ground squirrel.

Compared to arctic squirrels, desert squirrels face a different problem. These animals face problems posed by scorching summers rather than freezing winters. Temperatures can climb to more than 100°F. Food can become quite scarce. To survive, desert squirrels exhibit an innate behavior called **estivation**. An example is the Mohave ground squirrel that lives in the Mojave Desert in California. The squirrels sleep for about seven months a year in burrows when the air temperature gets above 98°F. They might go to sleep anytime from June to September and stay asleep until February. Males usually go into estivation first because they don't need to store as much food as the females do.

Reflexes

Have you ever stepped on a sharp object? If you have, then you realize that you immediately lifted your foot and perhaps grabbed it. You may have also yelled. You did all this without thinking about it. The behavior you exhibit when stepping on a sharp object is called a **reflex**. A reflex is another example of an innate behavior.

When you step on a sharp object, special cells in the foot known as pain receptors send signals to your spinal cord. Almost immediately, a signal is sent from your spinal cord to the foot. This signal causes you to lift your foot without thinking about doing it. Your brain is not telling your foot to move. In fact, by the time the signal reaches your brain, your foot has already been moved. However, when the signal reaches your brain, you begin to feel the pain. If you had to wait until your brain caused your foot to move, you may have been more seriously injured.

Learned Behavior

Not all behavior is innate. Some behavior is learned. **Learned behavior** is behavior that has been learned from experience or by observing other organisms. Learned behavior can modify or change innate behavior. For example, the tendency to make sounds is an innate behavior. However, the ability to speak words that have meaning is a learned behavior. Examples of learned behavior include the ability to speak English, Spanish, Italian, or any other language.

Humans are not the only animals that use sounds to communicate. Birds sing, wolves howl, dogs bark, and crickets chirp. Elephants learn how to communicate with low-pitched sounds that humans cannot hear. Humpback whales learn how to communicate with songs that can travel several miles through the water. Elephants and whales use these sounds to inform others of their location.

Conditioned Behavior

One of the most famous studies of learned behavior was done by a Russian scientist named Ivan Pavlov. Pavlov conducted his experiments on dogs during the late 1800s and early 1900s. Pavlov gave the dogs a meat powder. At the same time, he rang a bell. The dogs salivated. Salivating is an innate behavior. Pavlov repeated this process a number of times. He then rang the bell without giving the dogs any meat powder. The dogs still salivated. The dogs had become conditioned. The dogs learned to associate the sound of the bell with food. This type of learning is called **conditioned behavior**.

Survival Behaviors

Animals depend on the behavior, both innate and learned, to survive. An animal must exhibit various behaviors to stay alive. All these behaviors can be classified into several broad categories that are described in the following table.

Behavior Category	Purpose	Example
Defensive	Protection from predators	Turtle retreats into its shell.
Parental care	Survival of the young	Cat nurses her kittens.
Courtship	Attraction of a mate	Peacock spreads its tail.
Migratory	Location of a more suitable environment	Monarch butterflies travel from the United States to Mexico for winter.
Territorial	Protection of resources	Wolves form packs.
Foraging	Locate food	Owls hunt mice.

Lesson 6   Review

Darken the circle for the correct answer.

1. Innate behavior is determined by
Ⓐ experiences.
Ⓑ genes.
Ⓒ sounds.
Ⓓ weather.

2. Anything that causes a response is known as a
Ⓐ chemical.
Ⓑ gene.
Ⓒ behavior.
Ⓓ stimulus.

3. Which of the following is an example of a reflex behavior?
Ⓐ You ride your bicycle to school.
Ⓑ You answer a question in class.
Ⓒ You jump when the classroom door slams shut.
Ⓓ You finish your homework.

4. A migratory behavior occurs when an animal
Ⓐ moves to a new location.
Ⓑ seeks food.
Ⓒ defends itself from a predator.
Ⓓ learns how to survive.

5. Which of the following is an example of a territorial behavior?
Ⓐ a mouse hiding from a predator
Ⓑ a dog nursing her puppies
Ⓒ a wolf howling to chase away another wolf
Ⓓ a lion searching for food

6. Which of the following is not involved in a reflex?
Ⓐ brain
Ⓑ stimulus
Ⓒ spinal cord
Ⓓ response

7. Explain how a learned behavior differs from an innate behavior.
_____
_____
_____

8. Explain the difference between hibernation and estivation.
_____
_____
_____

Lesson 6, Review
Science 5, SV 9781419034336

Lesson 6   Hibernation and Estivation

The following graphs show the average high and low temperatures for one year at two national parks. Use these graphs to answer the questions that follow.

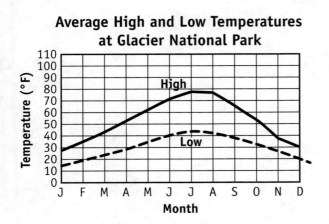

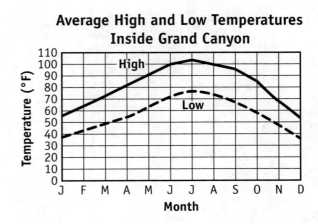

1. In which park are the animals more likely to hibernate? Explain the reason for your choice.

_____

_____

_____

2. During which three months are the animals most likely to hibernate?

_____

Lesson 6   Unscrambling Behavior

Below are boxes that contain one or two letters. Unscramble the boxes to form a phrase that deals with behavior.

1.

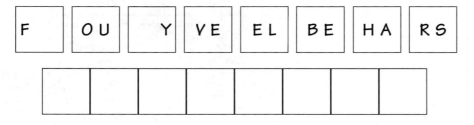

2.

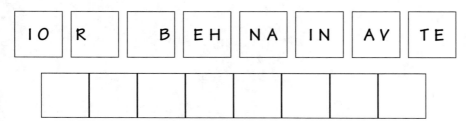

3.

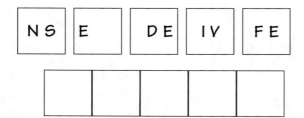

4.

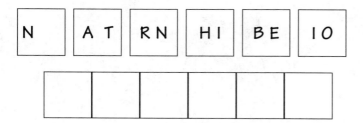

Lesson 6   Imprinting

Read the following passage and then answer the questions.

Imprinting is a type of behavior that includes both innate and learned behaviors. Imprinting is different from other types of learned behaviors. Imprinting occurs only during a certain time period in an animal's life. For example, young geese and ducks follow their mother to find food, seek shelter, and get water. However, these young geese and ducks must learn to recognize their mother. They learn as a result of imprinting.

Imprinting takes place shortly after the young geese and ducks hatch from their eggs. The young birds see their mother. The mother is likely to be the first object they see. The young birds identify themselves with their mother. They then will follow their mother wherever she goes.

However, experiments have shown that the young birds do not know that they should follow their mother. Rather, they respond to and identify with the first object they see. In the 1930s, a scientist named Konrad Lorenz raised a group of newly hatched birds to follow him wherever he went. He did this by making sure that he was the first object they saw after they hatched from their eggs. The young birds then imprinted on him. Once they did, they preferred to follow Lorenz wherever he went rather than follow their own mother. Since Lorenz's work, imprinting has been observed in other animals besides geese and ducks.

1. Which of the following statements is true about imprinting?
   - (A) Imprinting is a reflex behavior.
   - (B) Imprinting is a behavior that can be learned only during a certain time period in life.
   - (C) Imprinting is not a learned behavior.
   - (D) Imprinting is a territorial behavior.

2. If a rolling ball is the first object that newly hatched ducks see, then they will
   - (A) avoid any rolling balls they see later.
   - (B) follow any moving object they see.
   - (C) seek their mother.
   - (D) follow the rolling ball as if it were their mother.

3. Konrad Lorenz showed that
   - (A) all bird behavior is innate.
   - (B) imprinting can occur at any stage in a bird's life.
   - (C) birds can imprint on humans.
   - (D) food is a powerful stimulus.

4. Imprinting can occur
   - (A) between animals that look very different from one another.
   - (B) only between animals that resemble one another.
   - (C) only in geese and ducks.
   - (D) at any stage in an organism's life.

Lesson 6   Experiment: Bug Behavior

During the spring, summer, and fall, sow bugs can be found outdoors living under rocks, logs, and piles of leaves. Sow bugs are oval or slightly elongated with a flattened body that is about $\frac{1}{2}$ inch long. They are wingless, brownish or slate gray, and possess well-developed eyes, seven pairs of legs, and overlapping "armored" plates that make them look like little armadillos. Sow bugs have two tail-like structures on their rear end. In the following experiment, you will observe the behavior of sow bugs to determine if they prefer the dark or light.

You Will Need

scissors
cardboard
empty shoe box with lid
10 sow bugs (search outdoors or contact a local pet shop)
watch or clock
pencil
paper

Procedure

1. Cut a piece of cardboard that will divide the shoe box in half. Cut an opening in the cardboard "wall" large enough for sow bugs to pass through it. Place the cardboard inside the shoe box.

2. Cut the lid so that it covers one half of the shoe box.

3. Place five sow bugs in each half of the shoe box.

4. Place the lid so that it covers one side of the shoe box.

5. Count the number of sow bugs that are in each side of the shoe box after every minute for 15 minutes. Record your findings on a sheet of paper. You need to count only the ones that are in the open side of the shoe box. Subtract this number from 10 to determine how many are in the covered side.

Experiment: Bug Behavior (cont'd.)

Results and Analysis

Did more sow bugs collect in one side of the shoe box? If so, which side was it?

_____

_____

Conclusion

1. Do sow bugs prefer the light or dark environment? Explain your answer.

_____

_____

_____

_____

_____

_____

2. What benefit might there be in this behavior?

_____

_____

_____

_____

_____

_____

Lesson 7 Populations and Ecosystems

Have you ever seen a squirrel eating the nuts from an oak tree? Perhaps you have seen a bee feeding on the nectar of a flower. Or you may have seen a cat chasing after a mouse. All organisms need nutrients to survive. Nutrients supply the energy organisms need to grow and reproduce. Some organisms can make their own food or nutrients. Other organisms must eat to survive. In this lesson, you will learn that organisms are grouped based on how they get energy.

Producers

Some organisms can use sunlight to make food. Such organisms are called producers. A **producer** is an organism that makes food with the help of photosynthesis. Most producers are plants. However, algae and some bacteria are also producers. Plants are the main producers on land. Algae are the main producers in the ocean.

Consumers

Organisms that eat other organisms to obtain energy are called **consumers**. Consumers are not able to use the sun's energy to make food. Rather they must eat producers or other organisms. A consumer that eats a plant is called a **herbivore**. You are a herbivore when you eat celery, lettuce, spinach, or a tomato.

A consumer that eats an animal is called a **carnivore**. You are a carnivore when you eat a hamburger, hot dog, or bologna sandwich. Some organisms eat both plants and animals. Such a consumer is called an **omnivore**. Except for vegetarians, humans are omnivores.

Key Terms

producer—an organism that makes its own food with the help of photosynthesis

consumer—an organism that eats another organism

herbivore—an organism that eats only plants

carnivore—an organism that eats only animals

omnivore—an organism that eats both plants and animals

decomposer—an organism that gets energy by breaking down dead organisms

food chain—a simple diagram that shows the feeding relationships that exist in an ecosystem

ecosystem—all the living and nonliving things that are found in a particular area

food web—a diagram that shows the feeding relationships in an ecosystem

energy pyramid—a diagram that shows an ecosystem's loss of energy

Decomposers

Some organisms get energy by breaking down dead organisms. These organisms are called **decomposers**. Bacteria and fungi, such as mushrooms, are decomposers. Mushrooms break down dead branches and twigs. Most mushrooms that people eat are decomposers.

Decomposers break down the nutrients in dead organisms into simple materials, such as water and carbon dioxide. These simple materials can then be used by other organisms, including producers. Decomposers are nature's recyclers.

Food Chains

To understand the feeding relationships between organisms, scientists sometimes construct a diagram known as a food chain. A **food chain** is a simple diagram that shows the feeding relationships that exist in an ecosystem. An **ecosystem** is made up of all the living and nonliving things that are found in a particular area. For example, there may be a pond ecosystem in your local area. This pond ecosystem consists of all the organisms, both plants and animals, that live there. The pond ecosystem also consists of the nonliving things, such as the water and soil.

The following illustrates a food chain that can be found in a prairie.

grasses and seeds
↓
black-tailed prairie dog
↓
coyote

In the food chain, the grasses and seeds are the producers. The prairie dogs are herbivores because they eat the grasses and seeds. Notice that the arrow goes from the grasses and seeds to the prairie dog. This shows that the grasses and seeds are food for the prairie dog. The arrow also shows that energy stored in nutrients moves from the grasses and seeds to the prairie dog.

The coyotes are carnivores because they eat the prairie dogs. When any of these organisms die, bacteria and fungi in the soil decompose the remains and recycle the nutrients into the soil. The grasses can then use these recycled nutrients to make food. Therefore, the decomposers keep energy flowing through a food chain.

Food Webs

Feeding relationships are rarely as simple as they appear in a food chain. Rather, there are multiple producers, and a consumer usually depends on more than one source for food. In nature, one food chain is usually a part of another food chain. As a result, food chains usually connect with other food chains. These interconnected food chains make up a food web. A **food web** is a better illustration of how energy moves through an ecosystem. The food web on the next page illustrates the feeding relationships that exist in an ecosystem.

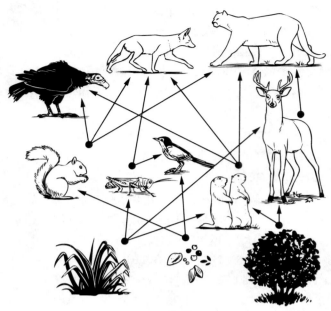

Notice that energy moves in only one direction, just as it does in a food chain. For example, energy moves from the prairie dog to the coyote in the above food web. Energy can also move from the prairie dog to the mountain lion. In addition to the prairie dog, deer and squirrels can also be eaten by a mountain lion. The mountain lion uses the energy it gets from eating. The mountain lion stores any energy that it does not immediately use.

Energy Pyramid

Grasses use most of the energy they get from the sun for their life processes. As living organisms, grasses carry out processes such as photosynthesis and reproduction. Because the grasses use most of the energy from the sun, only a little of the energy is available for the deer that feed on the grasses. In turn, the deer use most of the energy they get from the grasses for their life processes. As a result, only a little of the energy is available for the mountain lions that feed on the deer.

The end result is that less energy is available at each step. Therefore, there must be more grass than prairie dogs. There must also be more prairie dogs than mountain lions. The energy at each level in a food web can be diagrammed as an energy pyramid. An **energy pyramid** is a diagram that shows an ecosystem's loss of energy. The following illustration shows an energy pyramid.

Notice that an energy pyramid has a large base. This large base represents the large number of producers that are needed to support the higher levels. Notice also that an energy pyramid has a small top. This small top represents the small number of organisms that can be supported because only a little energy reaches the top. Both the amount of energy and the number of organisms decrease as you go up an energy pyramid.

An energy pyramid shows that an ecosystem is fragile. If damage is done to one level, then all organisms at higher levels will be affected. Damage to the base will affect every level. Damage to the base can also result in the elimination of a higher level. For example, if a forest is cleared of trees, then there may not be enough producers to support the consumers that live there.

Lesson 7   Review

Darken the circle by the best answer.

1. Which organism is a producer?
   - (A) grasshopper
   - (B) oak tree
   - (C) frog
   - (D) insect

2. Which diagram illustrates a carnivore eating a consumer?
   - (A) seeds → mice
   - (B) grass → marsh crab
   - (C) algae → snail
   - (D) spider → sparrow

3. What role do decomposers play in an ecosystem?
   - (A) They recycle nutrients.
   - (B) They produce food for other organisms.
   - (C) They store most of the energy.
   - (D) They provide energy to carnivores.

4. As you go up an energy pyramid, the number of organisms
   - (A) stays the same.
   - (B) increases.
   - (C) decreases.
   - (D) increases and then decreases.

5. An ecosystem contains
   - (A) only living things.
   - (B) only nonliving things.
   - (C) only producers.
   - (D) both living and nonliving things.

6. Both herbivores and carnivores are examples of
   - (A) consumers.
   - (B) producers.
   - (C) decomposers.
   - (D) omnivores.

7. A scavenger eats dead plants and animals. Therefore, a scavenger is an example of a(n)
   - (A) producer.
   - (C) decomposer.
   - (B) omnivore.
   - (D) food chain.

8. Draw a food chain that you might find in your local environment.

9. Examine the food web on page 72. What would happen to the other organisms if the coyotes were not part of this ecosystem?

_____

_____

Lesson 7

Finding Food

A gray wolf is hungry and looking for an elk. Can you find the path the wolf must follow to find its food?

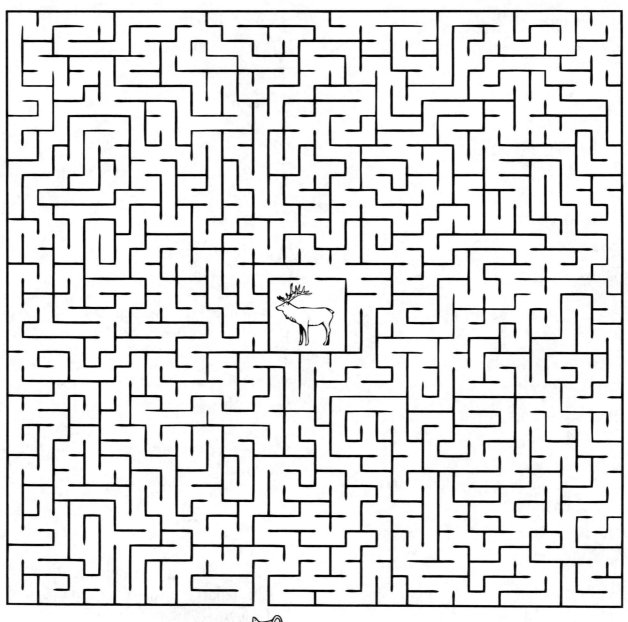

Lesson 7, Finding Food
Science 5, SV 9781419034336

Lesson 7 A Population and Ecosystem Crossword Puzzle

Across

4. shows several feeding pathways

6. shape used to show energy transfer between organisms

7. what a wolf is

8. organism that eats its vegetables

9. community of organisms and their nonliving environment

Down

1. organism that can make its own food

2. shows one feeding pathway

3. nature's recyclers

5. what you are when you eat a tunafish sandwich with lettuce and tomato

Lesson 7

Constructing a Food Chain

Number each of the following sets of organisms to construct a food chain that can be found in nature.

1.

Rabbit

_____

Lettuce

_____

Weasel

_____

2.

Woodmouse

_____

Owl

_____

Plant remains

_____

Lesson 7, Constructing a Food Chain
Science 5, SV 9781419034336

Lesson 7   An Energy Pyramid

Use the energy pyramid below to answer the questions that follow.

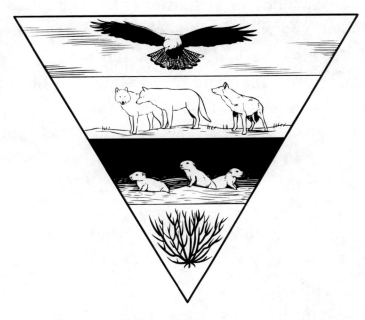

1. Which two levels contain the least amount of energy?

_____

2. Which two levels contain the most energy?

_____

3. Would an energy pyramid like the one shown above exist in nature? Explain your answer.

_____

_____

_____

4. How would you change the energy pyramid above so that it does represent one that exists in nature?

_____

_____

_____

Lesson 7, An Energy Pyramid
Science 5, SV 9781419034336

Lesson 7   Experiment: Making Your Own Food

You learned that a producer can make its own food with the help of photosynthesis. However, humans must consume other organisms, such as plants and animals, to survive. In this experiment, you will have the opportunity to act like a producer by making your own food. In this case, you will turn milk into cheese. Milk contains a lot of protein and a lot of water. The protein is dissolved in the water. To make cheese, you first change the protein so that it no longer is dissolved in the water. When this happens, the protein clumps to form a solid called curd. The leftover liquid part of the milk is called the whey.

You Will Need

stove
measuring cup
milk
saucepan
teaspoon
lemon juice
strainer
cheesecloth

CAUTION: Adult supervision required.

Procedure

1. Heat 8 ounces of milk in a saucepan until it just begins to boil.

2. Add 2 teaspoons of lemon juice to the milk. Stir the mixture once and remove it from the heat. Allow the mixture to cool for at least 15 minutes. The curd should separate from the whey.

3. Line the strainer with two or three layers of cheesecloth. Pour the mixture through the strainer over a sink. The curd should collect on the cheesecloth while the whey drains down the sink. Allow the curd to drain for 2 or 3 minutes.

4. Gather the edges of the cheesecloth and twist it over the sink. This will get out as much whey as possible.

Experiment: Making Your Own Food (cont'd.)

5. Open the cheesecloth. You have made your own food—cottage cheese. Enjoy!

Results and Analysis

Adding lemon juice changes the acidity of the milk and causes it to form curds. What happens as milk turns sour and curdles?

_____

_____

Conclusion

What conclusion can you draw based on your observations?

_____

_____

_____

_____

_____

Lesson 8 Diversity and Adaptations of Organisms

Millions of different organisms live on Earth. Scientists have identified and described about 1.5 million different kinds of organisms. Scientists are not sure how many more organisms remain to be discovered and identified. In addition, many more millions of organisms have become extinct. All these organisms are living proof of the great diversity of life on Earth.

Classification

Organizing things makes it easier to find something. Imagine how hard it would be to find a certain book in a library if the library was not organized using a logical system. Books are organized and grouped to make it easier for you to find the one you want. Scientists also organize and group organisms so that it is easier to study them.

Scientists use classification to organize the great diversity of life that exists. **Classification** is putting things into orderly groups based on similar characteristics. Every organism that has been discovered is classified according to its characteristics. Organisms that share similar characteristics are classified into the same group.

The first modern classification system was developed by a Swedish scientist named Carolus Linnaeus (1707–1778). Linnaeus developed a classification system for all 6000 species known at that time. A **species** is a group of organisms that can mate with one another and produce offspring. Linnaeus introduced some of the classification levels that are still used today.

Actually, classification started long before Linnaeus. More than 2000 years ago, the Greek philosopher Aristotle classified living things. His system placed organisms into one of two categories—animal or plant. He then divided the animals into three smaller groups, based on whether they lived in water, on land, or in the air.

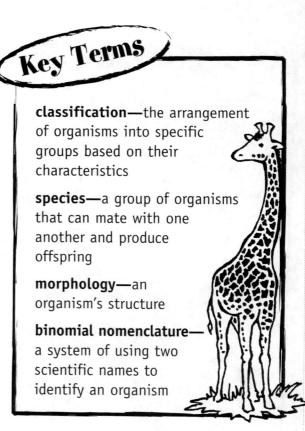

Key Terms

classification—the arrangement of organisms into specific groups based on their characteristics

species—a group of organisms that can mate with one another and produce offspring

morphology—an organism's structure

binomial nomenclature— a system of using two scientific names to identify an organism

For the most part, Linnaeus classified organisms based on their structure. This was an easy choice for Linnaeus to make. An organism's structure, or **morphology**, was easy to study. Besides, morphology was the only tool that Linnaeus had available to classify organisms.

Binomial Nomenclature

Linnaeus gave every organism he classified a scientific name. This was a major contribution to organizing the vast diversity of life that exists. Before Linnaeus, scientists often used common or local names when referring to an organism. But this practice could be very confusing. For example, what do you call the animal shown below?

Some people call it a panther, while others call it a mountain lion, and still others refer to it as a cougar or a puma. Scientists call it *Felis concolor*. An organism's scientific name consists of two parts. The first part of the name is the genus, and the second part is the species identifier. By custom, the genus name is capitalized, and both names are underlined or italicized.

This system of two-part names is known as **binomial nomenclature**. The use of binomial nomenclature eliminates any confusion about the identity of the organism. Linnaeus gave every organism he classified a two-part name. For example, the scientific name for a horseshoe crab is *Limulus polyphemus*.

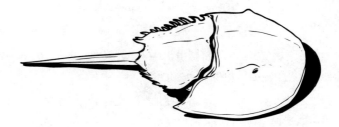

Horseshoe crabs spend most of the year in deep water. They leave the sea to mate along the beaches during high tide in warm weather. They can use their five pairs of legs to walk along the beach and also to swim on their back. An adult can grow up to two feet long. Horseshoe crabs have a hard external covering and a body that is divided into segments. These last two features are part of a horseshoe crab's morphology.

Based on its common name, you probably think that a horseshoe crab is classified in the same group as fiddler crabs, lobsters, and crayfish. Actually, horseshoe crabs are more closely related to spiders than they are to crabs. A closer look at a horseshoe crab's morphology reveals more similarities to spiders than to crabs. For example, horseshoe crabs do not have the jaws that other crabs have.

From Species to Kingdom

You learned that a species is a group of organisms that can mate and produce offspring. The species is the smallest and most specific group used for classifying living things. Species that share some features but still have certain features that are different are grouped together in the same *genus* (pl. genera). Genera that are similar are grouped together into a *family*. Several families of similar organisms are grouped into an *order*. Orders with similar features are grouped into a *class*. Classes that are similar are grouped into a *phylum* (pl. phyla). Phyla that are similar are grouped into the same *kingdom*. The following shows the classification levels, beginning with the species.

species → genus → family → order → class → phylum → kingdom

There are six kingdoms. These include Animals, Plants, Fungi, Protists, Eubacteria, and Archaebacteria.

Animal Kingdom

Members of the animal kingdom are complex organisms made up of many cells. These cells do not have a cell wall. Organisms in the animal kingdom can usually move around and quickly respond to their environment. Members of this kingdom include some unusual organisms such as sponges. At one time sponges were classified as plants because they do not move around. However, sponges do not make their own food. They must eat other organisms to get nutrients.

Plant Kingdom

Members of the plant kingdom can be simple or complex. All of them are made of cells that have a cell wall. In addition, members of this kingdom make their own food through photosynthesis. Familiar organisms that belong to this kingdom are trees and flowering plants. Scientists estimate that there are over 400,000 species of flowering plants alone.

Trees and flowering plants have structures that are usually associated with members of this kingdom—roots, stems, leaves, and seeds. However, not all members of the plant kingdom have these structures. Examples include mosses and ferns.

Fungus Kingdom

Members of this kingdom are organisms that are made up of many cells. These organisms do not move and cannot make their own food. Rather, fungi secrete chemicals into their surroundings. These chemicals break down the food into smaller pieces that the organism can absorb. Molds and mushrooms are examples of fungi.

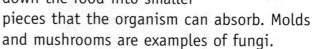

Protist Kingdom

Members of this kingdom can consist of just a single cell or of many cells. They can also be plantlike or animal-like. In fact, scientists sometimes place organisms into the protist kingdom simply because they do not fit into any other kingdom. Animal-like protists are commonly called protozoa. Plantlike protists are commonly known as algae. Some algae can get quite large, growing as tall as 200 feet in ocean waters.

Eubacteria Kingdom

Members of this kingdom are single-celled organisms that can be found almost everywhere on Earth. All the members are prokaryotes. You learned that such organisms lack a nucleus in their cells.

Archaebacteria Kingdom

Members of this kingdom are bacteria that live in extreme environments. No other living things can survive conditions where archaebacteria can thrive. For example, archaebacteria can survive the extreme heat of the hot springs in Yellowstone National Park.

Lesson 8

Review

Darken the circle by the best answer.

1. Which classification group contains the largest number of organisms?

   Ⓐ order

   Ⓑ class

   Ⓒ family

   Ⓓ phylum

2. What did Linnaeus use to classify organisms?

   Ⓐ their habitat or where they live

   Ⓑ the types of foods they eat

   Ⓒ their morphology

   Ⓓ the type of environment where they live

3. Which feature do all members of the plant kingdom share?

   Ⓐ cells that have a cell wall

   Ⓑ ability to move about

   Ⓒ consist of just a single cell

   Ⓓ secrete chemicals to break down food

4. Into which kingdom are the bacteria that live in your intestine classified?

   Ⓐ Archaebacteria

   Ⓑ Eubacteria

   Ⓒ Protist

   Ⓓ Fungus

5. The scientific name for the European water lily is *Nymphaea alba*. To which genus does this plant belong?

   Ⓐ water lily

   Ⓑ alba lily

   Ⓒ *alba*

   Ⓓ *Nymphaea*

6. Which classification group contains organisms that are most like one another?

   Ⓐ kingdom

   Ⓑ phylum

   Ⓒ species

   Ⓓ order

7. *Euglena* is a one-celled organism that can make its own food but does not have a cell wall. It can also ingest nutrients. How would you classify this organism? Explain your answer.

   _____

   _____

   _____

8. Explain why the use of scientific names is important to scientists.

   _____

   _____

Lesson 8   A Branching Diagram

The illustration below is known as a branching diagram. Several characteristics are listed along the line that points to the right. Each characteristic is shared by the animals to the right of it. For example, all the animals shown have hair and mammary glands.

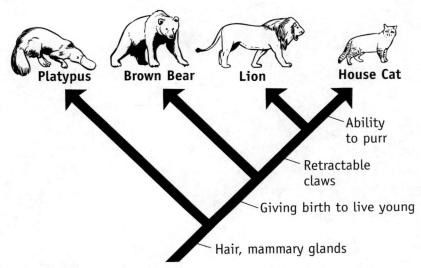

1. Which two animals are more closely related to each other than to the other animals? Explain your answer.

   _____

   _____

   _____

2. What characteristic does a brown bear have that a platypus does not possess?

   _____

3. Which animal is least similar to a house cat? Explain your answer.

   _____

   _____

4. What characteristic is used to separate the lion from the house cat?

   _____

Lesson 8

Classification Diagrams

The illustrations below show two different systems used to classify organisms. Use these diagrams to answer the questions that follow.

Classification system A

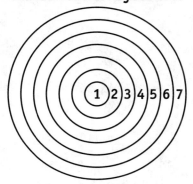

Classification system B

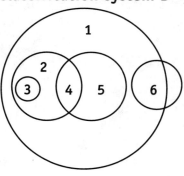

1. Which statement about Classification system A is true?

Ⓐ All organisms in group 1 are in group 7.

Ⓑ All organisms in group 7 are in group 1.

Ⓒ All organisms in group 5 are in group 4.

Ⓓ No organism can belong to more than one group.

2. Which statement about Classification system B is true?

Ⓐ All organisms in group 5 are in group 6.

Ⓑ All organisms in group 4 are in group 1.

Ⓒ All organisms in group 6 are in group 1.

Ⓓ No organism can belong to more than one group.

3. In Classification system B, what conclusion can you draw about group 4?

_____

_____

4. In Classification system A, which level would represent a kingdom? Explain your answer.

_____

Lesson 8

Amazing Survivors

Read the following passage and then answer the questions that follow the passage.

On April 20, 1967, the unmanned lunar spacecraft *Surveyor 3* landed on the surface of the moon. One of the things aboard was a television camera. On November 20, 1969, *Apollo 12* astronauts Pete Conrad and Alan Bean recovered the camera. When NASA scientists examined it back on Earth, they were surprised to find specimens of a bacterium called *Streptococcus mitis* that were still alive.

Because of the precautions the astronauts had taken, NASA could be sure that the bacteria did not come from the astronauts. Instead, the bacteria must have been inside the camera when *Surveyor 3* was launched. These bacteria had survived for 31 months in the vacuum of the moon's atmosphere until the astronauts retrieved the camera. The bacteria that survived on the moon suffered huge monthly temperature swings and the complete lack of water.

On May 19, 1995, *The New York Times* carried a front-page story about two scientists who had extracted bacteria from bees preserved in amber in Costa Rica. Amber is a tree sap that hardens and becomes a fossil. This amber had entrapped some bees and then hardened between 25 and 40 million years ago. Bacteria living in the bees' digestive system turned themselves into

spores. A spore is a reproductive cell that is protected by a thick cell wall. A spore can survive extremely harsh environmental conditions. By forming spores, these bacteria had been "asleep" for over 25 million years. They "awoke" only after the scientists removed them from the bees trapped in amber.

1. To what kingdom do you think the bacteria that survived on the moon and in amber belong? Explain your answer.

_____

_____

2. How do you think the bacteria survived on the moon for 31 months? Explain your answer.

_____

_____

3. Does this passage support the statement that prokaryotes can live in extreme environments? Explain your answer.

_____

_____

Lesson 8

A Kingdom Word Search

Can you find all six kingdoms in the following puzzle?

```
B O O O F B H R Z V I A A W J A G Q B J
B Q X L H B T T A A N Q G J Y M H X J W
B B Z I B Z O R A I K R O X E G N I J O
Z Z P M R R K W M K E D G T T X I P P U
T Y E T P T G A E J T Q Z K L I C U R J
U N D O U R L I S G N A E R C B Z K O P
W Y A S L E H F P A B M O B G C A T T I
U O O L Y E U U Z N S U G N U F Y F I X
R C J U P A K B O I L F E E N X N P S D
X J W F E H E C A X Z H I B N Q H M T X
A D G U Y W U B Q C I Y H J K J L V L F
E A B A Y E A U V E T M M C W I M L X D
S I V U P L I X N R Q E I O B K P E R E
L S F K O H X D H P P I R A Q D C U H O
W G S S Q A V I C G V R G I H H L M E G
J A R C H A E B A C T E R I A Y L Q W N
R P G U Z Q Q P V A N T F V P P W P L A
U Y B B J W Y U B M F Z A G D W P A Q B
B R Q D U X U L Q C K N J S O B N U V A
Q R R E K B Q I J G H V O R A Y B Q K L
```

Lesson 8, A Kingdom Word Search
Science 5, SV 9781419034336

Lesson 8

Experiment: Developing a Classification System

The following very unusual organisms were found on a remote Pacific island.

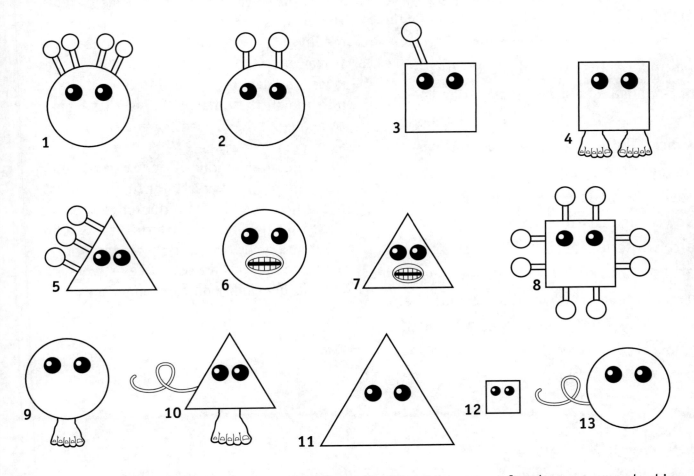

You have been assigned the job of developing a classification system for these strange-looking creatures. Start by placing all 13 creatures into one group. Then use some characteristic, such as shape, to divide this group into smaller ones. Continue dividing the groups until each group contains only one creature. You must use a different characteristic each time you form smaller groups. For example, you can use body parts and how many are present on a creature to form your groups. Describe your classification system on another sheet of paper.

Lesson 8, Experiment: Developing a Classification System
Science 5, SV 9781419034336

Lesson 9 Earth's History and Structure

Earth is a dynamic planet. Ever since it was formed about 4.5 billion years ago, Earth is constantly changing. Volcanoes erupt. Earthquakes occur both on land and under the sea. Landmasses are continuously changing position as they travel across the surface on huge masses of rock. These rock masses sometime collide, forming mountain ranges. At other times, the rock masses move apart, allowing molten rock to escape from Earth's interior. Despite all these changes, Earth remains divided into three layers. In this lesson, you will learn about these layers that form Earth and also about the atmosphere that surrounds it.

Crust

The outer layer, the **crust**, is made of rocks. The crust is the thinnest layer of Earth, ranging between 3 miles to 60 miles thick. It makes up only about 1 percent of Earth's mass. The deepest humans have ever drilled into the crust is about 10 miles. Its main components are oxygen, silicon, and aluminum.

There are two kinds of crust: continental crust and oceanic crust. **Continental crust** is the lighter, older, and thicker part of the crust that holds up the continents. **Oceanic crust** sits below the world's oceans. The oceanic crust has almost twice as much iron, magnesium, and calcium as the continental crust.

Key Terms

crust—the solid outermost layer of Earth

continental crust—the crust that forms landmasses, such as continents

oceanic crust—the crust that is found beneath the oceans

mantle—the layer of rock between Earth's crust and core

magma—hot, liquid rock

hydrothermal vent—an opening in the oceanic crust

lithosphere—the outermost rigid layer of Earth made of the crust and the solid upper part of the mantle

tectonic plate—a large block of the lithosphere

asthenosphere—the molten layer of the mantle on which tectonic plates move

core—the innermost layer of Earth

atmosphere—the mixture of gases that surrounds Earth

Mantle

Below the crust is the **mantle**. The mantle is much thicker than the crust and makes up about 67 percent of Earth's mass. It is about 1860 miles thick and contains mostly iron, magnesium, aluminum, and silicon. The upper part of the mantle is solid, but tremendous heat and pressure make the lower mantle act more like a thick liquid. This thick liquid rock is called **magma**.

Because no one has ever seen the mantle, scientists study its composition from observations made on Earth's surface. In some places, magma from the mantle rises to the surface. When a volcano erupts, magma may flow onto Earth's surface. Magma that flows onto Earth's surface is called *lava*. Lava can also rise to the surface from fissures, or cracks, in Earth's crust.

The ocean floor is another place where scientists can obtain information about the mantle. Active volcanoes on the ocean floor spew out magma. Magma from the mantle also rises up through the oceanic crust through openings known as **hydrothermal vents**. Scientists recently discovered a large area of these vents or chimneys in the middle of the Atlantic Ocean. This area was named the Lost City because it is found on an underwater mountain range called the Atlantis Massif. The Lost City's most distinctive feature is that it is sitting on a 1.5 million-year-old crust formed from mantle material. There are more than 30 vents in the Lost City. Not all of them are active and spew out magma from the mantle. The tallest one, named Poseidon, rises about 200 feet above the seafloor. The following diagram illustrates Earth's crust and mantle.

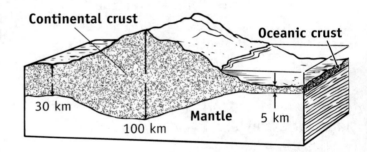

Continental crust
Oceanic crust
30 km
100 km
Mantle
5 km

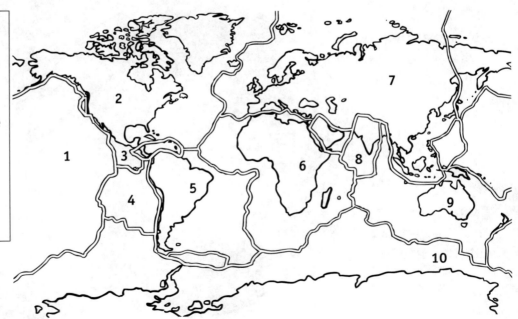

Major Tectonic Plates
❶ Pacific plate
❷ North American plate
❸ Cocos plate
❹ Nazca plate
❺ South American plate
❻ African plate
❼ Eurasian plate
❽ Indian plate
❾ Australian plate
❿ Antarctic plate

Tectonic Plates

The crust and the solid upper part of the mantle make up the lithosphere. The **lithosphere** is the uppermost part of Earth and includes all of the crust and the top of the mantle. The lithosphere is divided into giant moving chunks called **tectonic plates**. You can think of the lithosphere as a giant jigsaw puzzle. Each piece of the puzzle is a tectonic plate.

Tectonic plates float on a denser, molten layer of Earth known as the **asthenosphere**. The asthenosphere is a soft layer of the mantle made up of magma that flows slowly. The diagram on page 91 illustrates the major tectonic plates.

Notice that each tectonic plate fits together with the tectonic plates that surround it. Land plates, or *continental plates*, support the rocky landmasses of the continents. The North American plate, for example, contains most of the United States. *Oceanic plates* support the oceans. The Pacific plate, for example, sits mostly under the Pacific Ocean.

Not all tectonic plates are the same. As you just read, some are continental plates while others are oceanic plates. However, some plates are a mixture of these two types. For example, the South American plate lies under the South American continent and under part of the Atlantic Ocean. Therefore, the South American plate includes both continental plate and oceanic plate. In contrast, the Cocos plate is entirely an oceanic plate.

Tectonic plates also differ in size. The South American plate has an entire continent and part of the Atlantic Ocean sitting on it. In contrast, the Cocos plate has only a relatively small area of the Pacific Ocean above it.

Core

The innermost layer of Earth is called the **core**. It has a radius of about 2200 miles and makes up about 33 percent of Earth's mass. The core is mostly iron, with a little bit of nickel. Unlike the crust and mantle, the core contains almost no oxygen, silicon, aluminum, or magnesium.

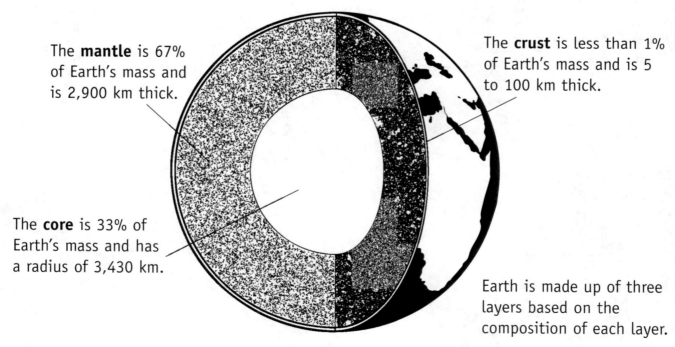

The **mantle** is 67% of Earth's mass and is 2,900 km thick.

The **crust** is less than 1% of Earth's mass and is 5 to 100 km thick.

The **core** is 33% of Earth's mass and has a radius of 3,430 km.

Earth is made up of three layers based on the composition of each layer.

The outer part is liquid, but enormous pressures keep the inner core solid. At the center of the core, the temperature is over 10,800°F. The pressure inside the core is four million times greater than at the surface. The diagram on page 92 illustrates Earth's crust, mantle, and core.

Earth's Atmosphere

Earth is surrounded by a layer of gases known as the **atmosphere**. Nitrogen is the most common gas in the atmosphere. This gas is released into the atmosphere when the remains of organisms break down. Volcanoes also release nitrogen into the atmosphere when they erupt.

Oxygen is the second most common gas in the atmosphere. Organisms use oxygen to carry out respiration. Respiration is the process organisms use to obtain energy they need to carry out their life processes. Together, oxygen and nitrogen make up about 99 percent of the atmosphere. The remaining 1 percent is made up of water, carbon dioxide, dust particles, sea salts, dirt, and smoke.

Like Earth, the atmosphere is made up of several layers. The lowest layer of the atmosphere is called the *troposphere*. The troposphere is the layer in which we and most organisms live. Temperatures vary greatly in the troposphere. As altitude increases, temperature decreases. As a result, snow can cover mountaintops throughout the year.

The layer above the troposphere is called the *stratosphere*. This is the layer of the atmosphere where jets fly. The upper stratosphere is made up of the ozone layer. The ozone layer protects life on Earth by absorbing harmful ultraviolet radiation from the sun. Scientists have recently become concerned about holes that have appeared in the ozone layer. Without the ozone layer, the radiation from the sun will reach Earth where it could damage an organism's DNA. Increased radiation from the sun would also increase cases of skin cancer.

Above the stratosphere is the *mesosphere*. This is the coldest layer of the atmosphere. Temperatures can be as low as −135°F. The uppermost layer of the atmosphere is the *thermosphere*. Temperatures in the thermosphere can reach 2700°F or higher. The space shuttle flies in the thermosphere.

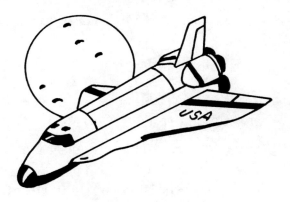

Lesson 9 Review

Darken the circle by the best answer.

1. Which layer of Earth is the thinnest?

  Ⓐ continental crust

  Ⓑ oceanic crust

  Ⓒ mantle

  Ⓓ core

2. Which is the part of Earth on which the tectonic plates move?

  Ⓐ lithosphere

  Ⓑ asthenosphere

  Ⓒ core

  Ⓓ oceanic crust

3. Which two layers of Earth make up the lithosphere?

  Ⓐ crust and mantle

  Ⓑ crust and core

  Ⓒ mantle and core

  Ⓓ oceanic crust and continental crust

4. Which layer of the atmosphere is closest to Earth?

  Ⓐ thermosphere

  Ⓑ mesosphere

  Ⓒ stratosphere

  Ⓓ troposphere

5. Where are hydrothermal vents found?

  Ⓐ Earth's core

  Ⓑ volcanoes

  Ⓒ ocean floor

  Ⓓ North American plate

6. Which two gases make up most of the atmosphere?

  Ⓐ oxygen and carbon dioxide

  Ⓑ nitrogen and oxygen

  Ⓒ nitrogen and carbon dioxide

  Ⓓ nitrogen and water vapor

7. How do scientists know about Earth's interior when they have never seen it?

_____

_____

8. Why is the ozone layer so important to life on Earth?

_____

_____

9. What is a tectonic plate?

_____

_____

Lesson 9

Complete the Sentences

Use the following list of words to complete each sentence. Each word may be used only once.

asthenosphere	hydrothermal vent	tectonic plate
atmosphere	lithosphere	thermosphere
core	magma	
crust	mantle	

1. Molten rock can rise up through a(n) _____, which is an opening in the oceanic crust.

2. The _____ is the innermost layer of Earth.

3. The space shuttle flies in space in a layer called the _____.

4. About 99 percent of the _____ is made up of nitrogen and oxygen gases.

5. The thin, solid layer of Earth is called the _____.

6. The crust and the rigid upper part of the mantle make up the

   _____.

7. A(n) _____ is a large block of the crust and the rigid, outermost part of the mantle.

8. The soft layer of the mantle on which tectonic plates move is called the

   _____.

9. The _____ consists of a layer of rock sandwiched between two other layers.

10. _____ that rises to the surface provides scientists with the opportunity to study Earth's interior.

Lesson 9   How Far Down Must You Go?

Suppose that you can travel to the center of Earth. Use the table below to answer the questions that follow.

Composition	Structure
Crust (50 km)	Lithosphere (150 km)
Mantle (2,900 km)	Asthenosphere (250 km)
	Mesosphere (2,550 km)
Core (3,430 km)	Outer core (2,200 km)
	Inner core (1,230 km)

1. How thick is the mantle?

_____

2. How far down would you have to go to reach Earth's innermost layer?

_____

3. How far down would you have to go to reach the center of the Earth?

_____

4. Is the crust described in this table oceanic crust or continental crust? Explain your answer.

_____

5. How far down would you have to go to find the structure on which tectonic plates move?

_____

Lesson 9   Unscrambling Earth

Each tile contains two, three, or four letters. Rearrange the tiles to form a term that deals with the structure of Earth.

1.

INEN	TALC	RUST	CONT

2.

TON	LAT	TEC	ICP	E

3.

LIT	PHE	RE	HOS

4.

HE	OT	VE	DR	HY	AL	RM	NT

5.

IN	UM	UM	AL

Lesson 9

Godzilla

Read the following passage and then answer the questions.

Hydrothermal vents exist in both the Pacific and Atlantic oceans. Most vents are found on the seafloor along the Mid-Ocean Ridge system, which is an underwater mountain chain that snakes its way around the globe.

Along the Mid-Ocean Ridge, the tectonic plates that form Earth's crust are moving apart, creating cracks in the ocean floor. Seawater seeps into these openings and is heated by the magma that lies beneath the crust. As the water is heated, it rises and seeks a path back out into the ocean through an opening in the seafloor.

As the vent water bursts out into the ocean, its temperature may be as high as 400°C (750°F). Yet this water does not boil because it is under so much pressure from the tremendous weight of the ocean above. When the pressure on a liquid is increased, its boiling point goes up.

Chimneys form on top of some hydrothermal vents. These chimneys can grow up to 9 meters (30 ft) in 18 months. A vent chimney called Godzilla reached the height of a 15-story building before it toppled.

There are several reasons why scientists want to learn more about hydrothermal vents. These underwater geysers are believed to play an important role in the ocean's temperature, chemistry, and circulation patterns. Scientists also are fascinated by the unusual life that inhabits vent sites. These creatures live in total darkness. However, they may light the way to the development of new drugs and other products useful to us all.

1. Godzilla was a(n)
   Ⓐ tectonic plate.
   Ⓑ underwater creature.
   Ⓒ chimney that formed on a hydrothermal vent.
   Ⓓ crack in the ocean floor.

2. Although it is extremely hot, water coming out a hydrothermal vent does not boil because of the
   Ⓐ darkness.
   Ⓑ circulation patterns.
   Ⓒ cracks in the oceanic crust.
   Ⓓ intense pressure.

3. Which statement about hydrothermal vents is true?
   Ⓐ Organisms live near these vents even though the water is extremely hot.
   Ⓑ They are found only in shallow waters.
   Ⓒ They are part of Earth's core.
   Ⓓ All hydrothermal vents are capped by huge chimneys.

4. What structure on Earth is like a hydrothermal vent in the ocean?
   Ⓐ forest
   Ⓑ iceberg
   Ⓒ geyser
   Ⓓ mountain

98

Lesson 9   Experiment: The Atmosphere

If you mention the word *fluid*, most people think of liquids such as water and milk. All liquids are fluids. However, not all fluids are liquids. A fluid is a substance that can flow. Liquids flow. Therefore, liquids are fluids. However, gases also flow. Therefore, gases are also fluids. Because the atmosphere is made of gases, then the air we breathe is a fluid. In the following experiment, you can demonstrate that air is a fluid by proving that it flows.

You Will Need

adult helper
matches
candle
plate
measuring cup
white vinegar
tablespoon
baking soda
poster board (12 inches by 4 inches)

Procedure

1. Ask your helper to light the candle and place it on the plate.

2. Add $\frac{1}{4}$ cup of white vinegar to the measuring cup.

3. Add 1 tablespoon of baking soda to the measuring cup.

4. Describe what happens.

5. Fold the poster board in half lengthwise to make a long trough.

6. Wait until the bubbling inside the measuring cup begins to slow down.

7. Hold the trough at an angle with one end near the candle. Be sure that the poster board does not touch the flame.

8. Use your free hand to pour the air inside the measuring cup down the trough. Be sure not to pour any liquid down the trough.

Experiment: The Atmosphere (cont'd.)

9. Describe what happens to the flame.

_____

_____

_____

Results and Analysis

1. What forms when you add the baking soda to the vinegar?

_____

2. The bubbles are made of carbon dioxide gas. Carbon dioxide is heavier than air, so it flows down the trough and replaces all the oxygen. A candle cannot burn without oxygen. How do you know the carbon dioxide gas flowed down the trough?

_____

_____

_____

Conclusion

What conclusion can you draw based on your observations?

_____

_____

_____

_____

Lesson 10 Earth in the Solar System

For almost five billion years, planets have been orbiting the sun. These planets and many moons and small bodies that orbit the sun make up our solar system. Our solar system is organized into smaller systems. One such system is made up of Earth and its moon. Other systems are larger. For example, Saturn is orbited by several moons that together make up the Saturn system. All these systems were formed from a cloud of gases that collected billions of years ago in space. In this lesson, you will learn how our solar system was formed.

The Formation of the Solar System

The solar system formed from a cloud of gases and dust called a **nebula**. Hydrogen and helium are the main gases. Carbon and iron particles make up most of the dust. A nebula is normally dark and cannot be seen in space. However, a nebula becomes visible when it is illuminated by light from nearby stars.

Our solar system formed from the **solar nebula**. Billions of years ago, this nebula collapsed because of gravity. You learned in Lesson 2 that gravity is a force of attraction between objects because of their mass. The gases and dust particles that make up a nebula are made of matter, which has mass. Because the gases and particles are very small, the attraction between particles in a nebula is very weak. In fact, the attraction is

just strong enough to keep the particles from drifting apart. The illustration below shows how the particles in a nebula are attracted to one another.

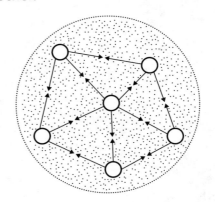

nebula—a large cloud of gases and dust in space

solar nebula—the nebula that formed our solar system

density—the ratio of the mass of a substance to its volume

star—an object in space that gives off light and that is made of extremely hot gases held together by gravity

nucleus—the central part of an atom that contains almost all its mass

nuclear fusion—the process in which two or more nuclei fuse, or join together, to form a larger nucleus

If gravity were the only force operating in a nebula, then all the particles should slowly collapse. However, as gravity pulls the particles closer, they begin bumping into one another. These collisions cause the particles to push away from one another. The illustration below shows how the particles in a nebula are pushed away from one another.

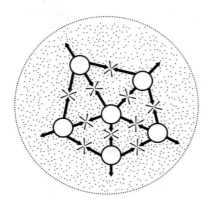

In a nebula, the inward force of gravity is balanced by the outward force created by collisions. As a result, the nebula keeps from collapsing. The illustration below shows how the forces are balanced between the particles in a nebula.

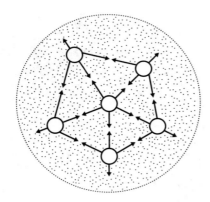

However, the forces in a nebula can be upset. This is what scientists think happened in the solar nebula. Perhaps another nebula crashed into the solar nebula. Or a nearby star may have exploded. In any case, some event occurred that pushed together the solar nebula. As the solar nebula collapsed, its density increased. **Density** is the ratio of the mass of a substance to its volume. The greater the density is, the more mass there is in a given volume. As the density increased, the attraction between the particles in the nebula also increased.

The center of the collapsing nebula became very dense and hot. The gases and dust particles slowly began to rotate around this center. This rotating movement helped balance the pull of gravity. The solar nebula slowly flattened into a rotating disk, like a Frisbee™ that is thrown through the air.

The Birth of Our Sun

Our sun is a star. A **star** is an object in space that gives off light and that is made of extremely hot gases held together by gravity. As the solar nebula collapsed, the center became dense and hot. When the center of the nebula stopped collapsing, our sun was born. The intense heat caused atoms of hydrogen gas to fuse together to form atoms of helium gas. This process continues today on the sun. This process is called nuclear fusion.

A **nucleus** is the central part of an atom that contains almost all its mass. In **nuclear fusion**, two or more nuclei fuse, or join together, to form a larger nucleus. In our sun, four hydrogen nuclei fuse to produce one helium nucleus. Each time this happens, an enormous quantity of energy is released.

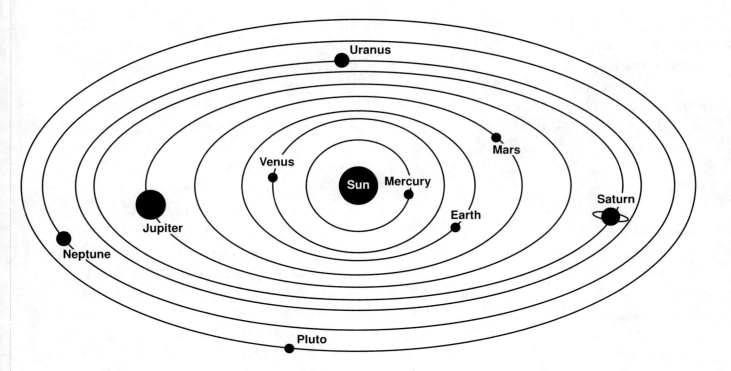

Nuclear fusion occurs in the center, or core, of the sun. The energy that is produced takes millions of years to reach the sun's surface. From there, the energy travels as light to Earth. This trip takes only 8.3 minutes and covers about 93 million miles.

The Birth of the Planets

As dust particles rotated around the center of the solar nebula, many of them collided. Some stuck together and formed larger particles. This process continued. As a result, the particles got larger and larger. They eventually grew to become bodies that were hundreds of miles wide. At this point, they became *planetesimals*, or small planets.

Some of these planetesimals continued to grow as particles collided and stuck to them. These planetesimals became planets. Other planetesimals collided with these planets as

they were forming. These collisions produced enormous craters.

Temperatures were too hot for gases to remain near the center of the solar nebula. Therefore, the hydrogen and helium gases collected near the outside of the rotating solar nebula. As a result, planets that formed in this region of the nebula became the gas giants. These planets include Jupiter, Saturn, Uranus, and Neptune. Despite the intense heat, rocky materials collected closer to the center of the nebula. As a result, planets that formed closer to the center formed mostly of rocky material. These planets include Mercury, Venus, Earth, and Mars.

Earth

Scientists think that Earth formed as a rocky planet within the first 10 million years of the collapse of the solar nebula. At first, the young planet most likely had an irregular shape, like a potato. However, as Earth grew larger, the force of gravity increased. Eventually, the force of gravity became so strong that it pulled rocky material toward its center. As a result, Earth started to become round.

As Earth continued to grow, its internal temperature rose faster than it could cool. The high temperatures melted the rocks inside. Today, volcanoes and earthquakes are the visible effects of these molten, or liquid, rocks trapped inside Earth.

As the rocks melted, denser materials sank toward the center of Earth. Less dense materials floated toward the surface. Eventually, three layers formed.  These layers are known as the crust, mantle, and core that you read about in the previous lesson. Earth's atmosphere, oceans, and continents eventually formed. Earth as we know it today began to take shape some 1.5 billion years ago.

Were You Counting?

You read that some planets are known as gas giants. These are called the outer planets and include Jupiter, Saturn, Uranus, and Neptune. You also read that some planets are known as rocky planets. These are called the inner planets and include Mercury, Venus, Earth, and Mars. If you count all these planets, there are eight. However, many books and museum displays show nine planets in our solar system. Which one is missing?

The missing one is Pluto, which was discovered in 1930. Pluto is the smallest planet and is the farthest one from the sun. Pluto's diameter is about 1400 miles, or about 700 miles less than the diameter of our moon. Pluto is so far from the sun that it takes about 248 years to make one revolution around the sun. By analyzing Pluto's density, scientists think that it is made of rock and ice.

Pluto is the only planet that has not been visited by a NASA mission. In January 2006, NASA launched a rocket to send a spacecraft on its way to Pluto. The spacecraft is scheduled to fly by Pluto and its tiny moon called Charon in 2015. However, seven months after NASA launched the spacecraft to Pluto, scientists decided that Pluto does not meet the new definition of a planet. To be classified as a planet, a celestial body must not cross the orbit of another body as it travels around the sun. Pluto's orbit crosses that of Neptune. As a result, Pluto has been reclassified in a new category of "dwarf planets." Other "dwarf planets" include Ceres, which was considered a planet in the 1800s, and UB313, which was discovered in 2003.

Lesson 10   Review

Darken the circle by the best answer.

1. Which planet is classified as an outer planet?

    Ⓐ Mercury

    Ⓑ Venus

    Ⓒ Saturn

    Ⓓ Earth

2. Scientists do not consider Pluto a planet because it

    Ⓐ is not part of our solar system.

    Ⓑ crosses the orbit of another planet.

    Ⓒ does not orbit the sun.

    Ⓓ cannot be seen from Earth.

3. Which force causes a nebula to collapse?

    Ⓐ gravity

    Ⓑ pressure

    Ⓒ magnetism

    Ⓓ electricity

4. How does the sun produce energy?

    Ⓐ by shrinking due to gravity

    Ⓑ by burning fuels

    Ⓒ by giving off light

    Ⓓ by nuclear fusion

5. Which two factors are included in density?

    Ⓐ temperature and pressure

    Ⓑ mass and volume

    Ⓒ size and shape

    Ⓓ diameter and mass

6. What is a planetesimal?

    Ⓐ comet

    Ⓑ asteroid

    Ⓒ small planet

    Ⓓ collapsing nebula

7. How do the inner planets differ from the outer planets?

    _____

    _____

    _____

8. How were the planets formed?

    _____

    _____

    _____

Lesson 10

The Planets I

Use the illustration below to answer the questions that follow.

1. What do these planets have in common?

_____

_____

2. In which direction do these planets revolve around the sun?

_____

_____

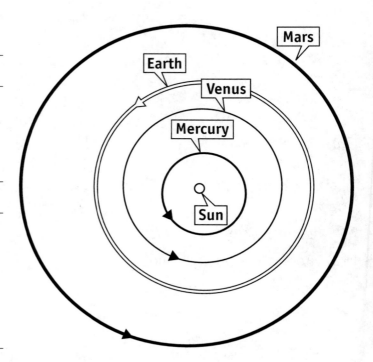

3. Mars's period of revolution around the sun is 1 year and 322 days. Mercury's period of revolution is only 88 days. Explain this difference.

_____

_____

4. Is Mars always the same distance from the sun? Explain your answer.

_____

_____

5. The surface temperature of Mercury can approach 800°F. Explain why.

_____

_____

Lesson 10   The Planets II

Use the illustration below to answer the questions that follow.

1. What do these planets have in common?

   _____

   _____

2. One of these planets is not like the others.
   Which one is it? How is it different?

   _____

   _____

3. The shortest period of revolution for one of
   these planets is 11 years and 313 days.
   Which planet is this? Explain your answer.

   _____

   _____

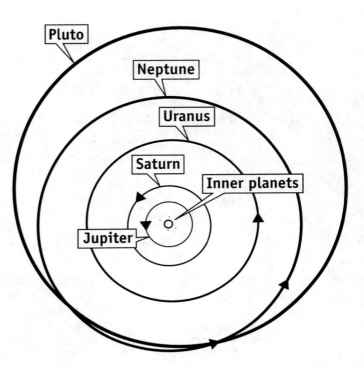

4. Which planet would you expect has the lowest surface temperature—Uranus, Saturn, or
   Neptune? Explain your answer.

   _____

   _____

Lesson 10, The Planets II
Science 5, SV 9781419034336

Lesson 10   Comparing the Planets

Use the following table to answer the questions about the planets.

Planet	Diameter	Density	Surface gravity
Earth	12,756 km	5.52 g/cm^3	100% of Earth's
Venus	12,104 km	5.24 g/cm^3	91% of Earth's
Saturn	120,536 km	0.69 g/cm^3	92% of Earth's
Neptune	49,528 km	1.64 g/cm^3	112% of Earth's
Mars	6,794 km	3.93 g/cm^3	38% of Earth's
Jupiter	142,984 km	1.33 g/cm^3	236% of Earth's

1. Weight depends on the force of gravity. On which planet(s) would a person weigh more than on Earth? Explain your answer.

_____

_____

2. Three of the planets in the table above are inner planets, while the other three are outer planets. What information in this table can be used to identify which are the inner planets and which are the outer planets?

_____

_____

3. Which two planets are most similar? How are they similar?

_____

_____

4. Saturn is about 10 times larger than Earth. How can you then explain the difference in their densities?

_____

_____

Lesson 10   Planet X

Read the following passage and then answer the questions.

In 1930, scientists knew that eight planets orbit the sun. However, they suspected that a ninth planet, which they called Planet X, existed. Scientists thought that Planet X was in an orbit beyond Neptune, which at that time was the farthest known planet from the sun. After searching the skies for more than eight months, an American scientist named Clyde Tombaugh thought he had found Planet X. The date was February 18, 1930.

When searching for a new planet, scientists measure the parallax of an object in space. Parallax is the apparent movement of an object when it is viewed from two different positions. Every day, Earth travels about 1.6 million miles in its orbit around the sun. In just six days, Earth travels about 10 million miles in space. Looking at the night sky six days apart is viewing space from two positions that are about 10 million miles apart! During these six days, stars will remain in fixed positions. However, a planet will appear to move through the night sky. This is exactly what Tombaugh saw in photographs he had taken through his telescope six nights apart.

Tombaugh carefully measured the distances between the images on the two photographs. One of the hundreds of light spots had moved about one-eighth of an inch. Tombaugh decided to take more photographs. These photographs also showed

an object moving through the night sky. On March 12, 1930, Tombaugh announced to the world that he had discovered Planet X. He wanted to name the planet Minerva, but that name had already been given to an asteroid. An eleven-year-old girl living in England sent Tombaugh a letter. She suggested that the planet be called Pluto.

1. Why did Tombaugh photograph the same spot in the night sky six days apart?

   _____

   _____

   _____

2. Why did Tombaugh take more photographs after he had observed the moving object the first time?

   _____

   _____

   _____

3. Why was Pluto the last planet to be discovered?

   _____

   _____

   _____

Lesson 10   Experiment: Blasting Off

Most of our knowledge about the solar system comes from NASA missions. These missions include the space shuttle, unmanned probes, and special instruments such as the Hubble Telescope that are launched into space. Rockets are used to launch all these missions. In the following experiment, you will build a rocket and see how far into space you can launch it.

You Will Need

tape
toilet paper tube
paper plate
tablespoon
white vinegar
film canister (one where the cap fits inside the rim)
teaspoon
baking soda

CAUTION: Adult supervision required.

Procedure

1. Tape the toilet paper tube to the center of the plate. This will serve as your rocket launcher.

2. Add one tablespoon of vinegar to the film canister. The canister will serve as your rocket.

3. Add $\frac{1}{2}$ teaspoon of baking soda to the canister.

4. As quickly as you can, snap the lid on the canister. Drop the canister down the tube. Make sure that the lid side is down.

5. Stand back and watch what happens.

6. If your rocket does not launch, wait at least one minute before you check it.

7. Rinse the canister with water and repeat steps 2–5.

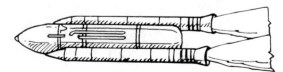

Experiment: Blasting Off (cont'd.)

Results and Analysis

1. Mixing the vinegar and baking soda produces a gas. More and more gas collects inside the film canister. Eventually, the gas pops the lid off the canister. This creates a force. What does this force do?

_____

_____

2. Experiment with your "rocket fuel." Try changing the proportions you use to mix the vinegar and baking soda. Try using water and a crushed antacid tablet as your "rocket fuel." Which fuel propels your rocket the farthest into space?

_____

_____

Conclusion

What conclusion can you draw based on your observations?

_____

_____

Science Fair Projects

Although they are at the end of the lessons, the experiments in this book should be the beginning for learning something about science. You may have done the experiment titled *Blasting Off*. You may have successfully launched your rocket so that it soared into the sky by finding out which fuel worked best. But you can also experiment with the rocket itself. You could try cutting poster board to make fins and a nose cone for the film canister to find out if it will soar even higher. You could also try using warm vinegar with the baking soda or warm water with the antacid tablet. You can even do some research to see if you can come up with a better fuel. In other words, you should be creative, like any good scientist.

Designing an Experiment

If you design your own experiment, be sure that you do so safely and correctly. You must carry out all your work with the supervision of an adult, either your parent or teacher. The adult must help with any procedure that involves a risk. For example, the experiment may require the use of a sharp knife or hot stove. The adult should perform these steps. In addition, you must have an adult review the materials you will use and the procedure you will follow *before* you begin any experiment or science fair project. You should wear safety goggles, tie back long hair, and avoid wearing loose clothing. Never taste, touch, or smell anything unless an adult has given you permission. Do not eat or drink around your experiment. Always use precautions to keep yourself safe.

Also be sure that your experiment has been designed correctly. Whenever a scientist designs an experiment, he or she always includes a control. A **control** is used so that only one factor or variable is present in the experiment. A **variable** is anything that changes.

You may have done the experiment titled *Bug Behavior*. The experiment is designed to determine if the bugs prefer the light or darkness. The container must be set up so that one half is in light and the other half is in darkness. All other conditions must be the same on both sides. One side cannot contain food, a place to hide, or water. If the bugs are found in one area, then you can make a valid conclusion as to whether they prefer the light or darkness. In this experiment, the only variable was the presence or absence of light. No other factor was introduced into the experiment.

Choosing a Project

Any experiment in this book can serve as the basis for a science fair project. Usually, doing a science fair project is a bit more involved than carrying out an experiment. Rather than use an experiment in this book as your starting point, you may want to pick your own topic to investigate. If you do, you will have to do some research to learn something about the topic. This research can involve checking the Internet, reading books, and talking to teachers and scientists. A good place to begin is to think about what you like. For example, if you like building models, then you may want to build a model that explains a scientific principle or concept. Models were used in Lesson 1 to explain the difference between solids, liquids, and gases. You can build a model to show what happens as water freezes to explain why ice floats.

Deciding what to do for a science fair project is often the hardest part of the project. Read the following ideas to help you get started. After you have decided on your project, you will have to obtain more information to carry it out. You can get this information from the Internet, the library, or your teachers. You can also check companies that sell to individuals for items that can help you with your project.

Lesson 1 Properties and Changes of Properties in Matter

- **Surface Tension**—Check which liquid has the greatest surface tension. The more paper clips a liquid can support, the greater its surface tension. Liquids to test include water, rubbing alcohol, vinegar, and milk. Also test what happens to surface tension when you add some liquid detergent.
- **Melting Curve**—Measure the temperature as a solid melts. You can use ice cubes and a candle. Be sure to continue heating after the ice cubes have completely melted. Plot the melting curve for ice and compare it to the cooling curve from the experiment in this lesson.
- **Temperature and Gases**—Test how changes in temperature affect the volume of a gas. This can be done

simply by seeing what happens to the size of a balloon as it is cooled by placing it inside a refrigerator. Or you can design a project to measure the volume of a gas as the temperature changes.

Lesson 2 Motions and Forces

- **Friction**—Test various methods to increase and reduce friction. Time how long it takes for an object to roll down an inclined board. Cover the board with different materials to check how they affect friction.
- **Forces**—Demonstrate how an object will move if only an unbalanced force is applied. Measure the forces that were applied to the object. To measure the force, you will need to construct a device from rubber bands and a ruler.
- **Gravity**—Prove that all objects have the same acceleration due to gravity. You will have to time how long it takes for objects of different masses to fall from a considerable height. You will also have to consider the factor of air resistance.

Lesson 3 Transfer of Energy

- **Kinetic Energy**—Calculate the kinetic energy of various moving objects. The formula for calculating kinetic energy requires that you know both their mass and velocity.
- **Potential Energy**—Calculate the potential energy that is stored in a food such as a peanut. You will have to build a calorimeter and measure the temperature change of a sample of water as the food burns.

- **Electrical Energy**—Demonstrate the difference between static electricity and current electricity. Relate static electricity to lightning. Relate current electricity to voltage, resistance, and amperes.

Lesson 4 Structure and Function in Living Things

- **Photosynthesis**—Extract the chlorophyll from a green plant. Use the process of chromatography to separate the chlorophyll into its various pigments. Use chromatography to separate other types of mixtures such as marker inks.
- **Diffusion and Osmosis**—These are two processes by which substances, such as water, enter and leave the cell. Demonstrate what happens as a result of diffusion and osmosis using a freshwater plant known as elodea. Experiment with ways of changing the rate at which these processes occur.
- **The Cell**—Make a three-dimensional model of the cell showing the various structures it contains. Distinguish between those structures found in an animal cell and those present in a plant cell.

Lesson 5 Reproduction and Heredity

- **DNA**—Extract or take out the DNA from various cells including spinach, broccoli, and chicken liver. Show what DNA looks like. A detergent is needed. Experiment to find out which detergent works best.
- **Regeneration**—Study how organisms are able to regenerate missing body parts. Planaria, a freshwater flatworm, is an excellent organism to use. This organism will regenerate so that it has two or even three heads on one body.
- **Seeds**—Find out why roots grow downward and stems grow upward as seeds germinate. Plant responses to the environment are called tropisms. Plant responses to gravity are called geotropism.

Lesson 6 Regulation and Behavior

- **Reflex Behavior**—Test reflex response time. Select a reflex behavior such as having a person press a switch after hearing a sound. Find out if reflex time is affected by a factor such as age, time of day, or surroundings.
- **Pheromones**—A pheromone is a substance that is released by an organism. Pheromones cause another individual to behave in a predictable way. Pheromones are used as bait to trap insects. Design a project to test how well a particular pheromone works.
- **Model of Hibernation**—Use a small organism known as daphnia to see how body processes are affected by temperature. Use a microscope to measure heart beat rate as the temperature is raised and lowered.

Lesson 7 Populations and Ecosystems

- **Ecosystem**—Set up a self-sustaining ecosystem in an aquarium tank. Such a system does not require anything to be added or removed. As a result, you will need producers, consumers, and decomposers. Explain the role of each organism in your ecosystem.

- **Hydroponics**—Grow plants (producers) without soil. This technology is called hydroponics. Include information about where and how this technology is being used.
- **Food Chain**—Use owl pellets to construct a food chain. These pellets contain undigested materials from an owl's diet. Resources will be needed to identify the source of the remains that include bone fragments and hair.

Lesson 8 Diversity and Adaptations of Organisms

- **Identifying Organisms**—An organism is sometimes identified with the help of a dichotomous key. Develop your own dichotomous key that can be used to identify a variety of either plants or animals.
- **Taxonomy**—The science of describing, classifying, and naming organisms is called taxonomy. In some cases, organisms are reclassified as new information is discovered. Prepare a report on organisms that have been reclassified and explain why.
- **Bacteria**—A variety of consumer products, especially soaps, contain an antibacterial ingredient. Conduct a project to determine the effectiveness of these products in preventing bacterial growth. You will have to learn how to grow bacteria in culture dishes.

Lesson 9 Earth's History and Structure

- **The Atmosphere**—Prove that the atmosphere contains about 21 percent oxygen. Include some history of science in your project by describing the contribution of Antoine Lavoisier to our knowledge of oxygen.
- **Tectonic Plates**—Some scientists think that tectonic plates move because of convection currents. Build a working model to show how a convection current is produced and how it could move a tectonic plate.
- **Earth's Structure**—Construct a model of Earth's layers shown in scale. Include information about each of the five physical layers.

Lesson 10 Earth in the Solar System

- **The Sun**—Demonstrate that sunlight is needed for photosynthesis to occur. Develop your project to show which wavelengths of light are most effective.
- **Measuring Distances in Space**—Build a solar-distance measuring device to calculate how far the sun is from Earth. You can find everything you need right at home. The math involved is simple.
- **Telescope**—This device has provided much information about our solar system. Construct a simple telescope. Use it to make observations of objects in the sky. Prepare a report summarizing your observations.

Presenting Your Project

Students usually present their projects in the form of a three-sided display. This display should include all the important information about your project. The left side of the display can include any background information you obtained from the Internet, books, or people. You can also place the purpose and procedure of your project on this side.

The center panel on your display should include the title of your project, your name, and grade at the top. All your results should be shown on this center panel. Do not display your results simply by showing what you wrote. Also include photographs, drawings, graphs, and other visual materials to help show what you found.

The right side of the display usually includes your conclusion and explanation. Your display will be more impressive if you include the setup you used in your project or any models that you built. These items are usually displayed on the tabletop in front of the display.

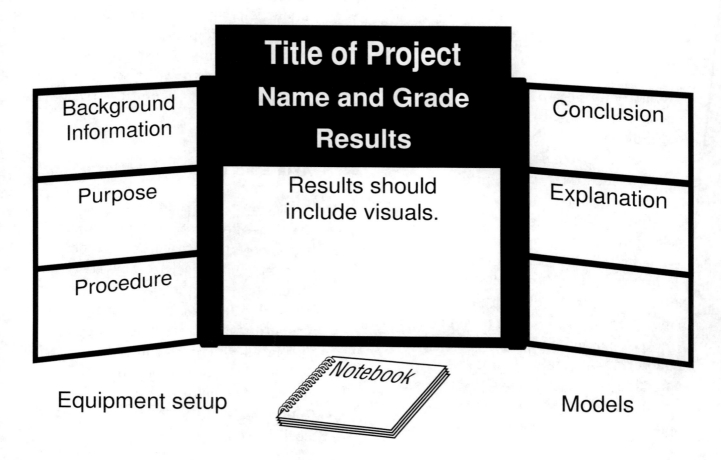

Procedure

When it is time to present your project, take your time in explaining what you did. Start with the information displayed on the left panel, then move on to the center panel, and then finally review what is shown on the right-hand panel. Be sure to impress your listener with what you learned and how much fun you had while doing your science fair project.

Glossary

acceleration—the rate at which velocity changes (p. 18)

anther—the tip of a stamen (p. 51)

asexual reproduction—the process by which a single parent produces offspring that are identical to the parent (p. 51)

asthenosphere—the molten layer of the mantle on which tectonic plates move (p. 90)

atmosphere—the mixture of gases that surrounds Earth (p. 90)

atom—the building block of matter (p. 7)

behavior—an action or series of actions that an animal performs in response to a stimulus (p. 60)

binary fission—a type of asexual reproduction in which one single-celled organism copies itself to form two single-celled organisms (p. 51)

binomial nomenclature—system of using two scientific names to identify an organism (p. 80)

boiling point—the temperature at which a liquid turns into a gas (p. 7)

budding—a type of asexual reproduction in which a part of the parent pinches off and forms a new organism (p. 51)

carnivore—an organism that eats only animals (p. 70)

cell—the smallest unit that can perform all life processes (p. 40)

cell membrane—the protective layer that covers a cell's surface and controls what enters and leaves a cell (p. 40)

cell wall—a rigid structure that gives support to a plant cell (p. 40)

change of state—the change of a substance from one physical form to another (p. 7)

chemical energy—the energy of a substance that changes as its atoms are rearranged (p. 30)

chlorophyll—a green substance that traps sunlight for photosynthesis (p. 40)

chloroplast—the structure where a plant cell makes food (p. 40)

classification—the arrangement of organisms into specific groups based on their characteristics (p. 80)

condensation—the change of state from a gas to a liquid (p. 7)

condensation point—the temperature at which a gas turns into a liquid (p. 7)

conditioned behavior—a behavior that has been modified so that it occurs when another stimulus is substituted for the original stimulus (p. 60)

consumer—an organism that eats another organism (p. 70)

continental crust—the crust that forms landmasses, such as continents (p. 90)

core—the innermost layer of Earth (p. 90)

crust—the solid outermost layer of Earth (p. 90)

cytoplasm—the fluid and most of the structures inside a cell (p. 40)

DNA—the chemical substance that controls the structure and function of cells (p. 51)

decomposer—an organism that gets energy by breaking down dead organisms (p. 70)

density—the ratio of the mass of a substance to its volume (p. 101)

ecosystem—all the living and nonliving things that are found in a particular area (p. 70)

egg—the female sex cell (p. 51)

electrical energy—the energy of moving electrons (p. 30)

electron—an atomic particle that has a negative charge (p. 30)

energy—the ability to do work (p. 7)

energy conversion—the change of one form of energy to another (p. 30)

energy pyramid—a diagram that shows an ecosystem's loss of energy (p. 70)

estivation—a period of decreased activity that some animals undergo during the summer (p. 60)

eukaryotic cell—a cell that has a nucleus (p. 40)

fertilization—the joining of an egg and sperm (p. 51)

food chain—a simple diagram that shows the feeding relationships that exist in an ecosystem (p. 70)

food web—a diagram that shows the feeding relationships in an ecosystem (p. 70)

force—a push or pull on an object (p. 18)

freezing point—the temperature at which a liquid turns into a solid (p. 7)

friction—a force that opposes motion between two surfaces that are in contact (p. 18)

gas—the state of matter that has no definite shape or definite volume (p. 7)

gene—a set of instructions that determines a trait an organism will have (p. 60)

gravity—a force of attraction between two objects (p. 18)

heat—the energy transferred between objects that are at different temperatures (p. 30)

herbivore—an organism that eats only plants (p. 70)

hibernation—a period of decreased activity that some animals undergo during the winter (p. 60)

hydrothermal vent—an opening in the oceanic crust (p. 90)

innate behavior—a manner of acting that does not depend on learning or experience (p. 60)

joule—the unit for work (p. 30)

kinetic energy—the energy an object has because of its motion (p. 30)

learned behavior—a behavior that has been learned from experience or by observing other organisms (p. 60)

light energy—the energy produced by the vibrations of electrically charged particles (p. 30)

liquid—the state of matter that has a definite volume but takes the shape of its container (p. 7)

lithosphere—the outermost rigid layer of Earth made of the crust and the solid upper part of the mantle (p. 90)

magma—hot, liquid rock (p. 90)

mantle—the layer of rock between Earth's crust and core (p. 90)

mass—the amount of matter in an object (p. 7)

matter—anything that has both volume and mass (p. 7)

mechanical energy—the total energy of motion and position of an object (p. 30)

melting point—the temperature at which a solid turns into a liquid (p. 7)

morphology—an organism's structure (p. 80)

motion—the change in position of an object over time with respect to a reference point (p. 18)

nebula—a large cloud of gases and dust in space (p. 101)

newton—the unit for force (p. 18)

nuclear energy—the energy produced when matter is changed into energy (p. 30)

nuclear fusion—the process in which two or more nuclei fuse, or join together, to form a larger nucleus (p. 101)

nucleus—the cell structure that controls several functions, including reproduction (p. 40); the central part of an atom that contains almost all its mass (p. 101)

oceanic crust—the crust that is found beneath the oceans (p. 90)

omnivore—an organism that eats both plants and animals (p. 70)

organism—a living thing (p. 40)

photosynthesis—the process by which a plant cell makes food (p. 40)

pistil—the female reproductive structure of a flower (p. 51)

pollen—the tiny structures in which sperm form (p. 51)

potential energy—the energy an object has because of its position (p. 30)

producer—an organism that makes its own food with the help of photosynthesis (p. 70)

prokaryotic cell—a cell that does not have a nucleus (p. 40)

reflex—an innate behavior that involves an involuntary response to a stimulus (p. 60)

regeneration—a type of asexual reproduction in which a part of an organism breaks off and develops into a new individual (p. 51)

sexual reproduction—the process by which offspring are produced when the sex cells from two parents unite (p. 51)

solar nebula—the nebula that formed our solar system (p. 101)

solid—the state of matter that has a definite shape and a definite volume (p. 7)

sound energy—the energy produced by the vibrations of an object (p. 30)

species—a group of organisms that can mate with one another and produce offspring (p. 80)

speed—the distance traveled by an object divided by the time it takes to travel that distance (p. 18)

sperm—the male sex cell (p. 51)

stamen—the male reproductive structure of a flower (p. 51)

star—an object in space that gives off light and that is made of extremely hot gases held together by gravity (p. 101)

state of matter—the physical form in which a substance can exist (p. 7)

stigma—the tip of a pistil (p. 51)

stimulus—anything that causes a response (p. 60)

surface tension—a force that holds together the particles of a liquid at its surface (p. 7)

tectonic plate—a large block of the lithosphere (p. 90)

thermal energy—all the kinetic energy due to the random motion of the particles that make up an object (p. 30)

velocity—the speed of an object in a particular direction (p. 18)

volume—the amount of space taken up, or occupied, by an object (p. 7)

weight—a measure of the force of gravity on the mass of an object (p. 7)

work—the use of a force that causes an object to move in the direction of the force (p. 30)

zygote—the cell produced when an egg and sperm unite (p. 51)

Answer Key

Assessment, pp. 5–6
1. D	**2.** C	**3.** D	**4.** B
5. A	**6.** B	**7.** C	**8.** D
9. A	**10.** B	**11.** A	**12.** D
13. A	**14.** C	**15.** A	**16.** C

Unit 1, Lesson 1
Review, p. 12

1. B	**2.** A	**3.** D
4. C	**5.** A	**6.** B

7. As a substance melts, the particles have more energy. They move farther apart from one another and can move past one another as the liquid forms. As a result, they are less ordered in a liquid as compared to a solid.

8. The particles of a liquid are free to move past one another, allowing them to take the shape of the container.

Models, p. 13

1. Model B. The particles in this model are not tightly held together and therefore can move past one another.

2. Model A and D. These models represent gases where the particles have the most energy and therefore can move far apart from one another.

3. The shape and volume will remain the same because model C represents a solid.

4. Models A, B, and D. At the boiling point, both the liquid and gas are present. Models A and D represent a gas, while model B represents a liquid.

Solids, Liquids, and Gases, p. 14

Hot Air Balloons, p. 15
1. C	**2.** B	**3.** D	**4.** A

Experiment: Freezing Water, p. 16
Results and Analysis:
The temperature of the water drops as it is cooled. However, the temperature levels off as ice begins to form. Once the water has completely frozen, the temperature will again begin to drop.
Conclusion:
The temperature of a substance does not change as it undergoes a change in state.

Unit 1 Lesson 2
Review, pp. 22–23

1. C	**2.** D	**3.** B	**4.** D
5. A	**6.** C	**7.** C	

Answer Key
Science 5, SV 9781419034336

Answer Key cont'd.

8. 400 mi/h
9. She may change her direction by turning her bicycle.
10. No. The forces acting on the box are balanced forces.

Motions and Forces, p. 24
1. d 2. e 3. g 4. f or h
5. i 6. b 7. i 8. a
9. f or h 10. a, c, g, i

Balanced and Unbalanced Forces, p. 25
1. B 2. D 3. C

Speed, Velocity, and Acceleration, p. 26
1. 5 miles
2. They had different velocities; they were heading in different directions.
3. 50 mi/h
4. 50 mi/h west
5. The acceleration changed whenever the car decreased its speed, increased its speed, or turned.

Motion and Forces Crossword Puzzle, p. 27
Across
4. velocity
6. motion
7. unbalanced
10. friction
Down
1. speed
2. gravity
3. acceleration
5. time
8. newton
9. force

Experiment: Detecting Acceleration, p. 29
Results and Analysis
1. First, the cork quickly moves in the direction the bottle is pushed and then swings backward.
2. The accelerometer accelerates whenever the speed or direction is changed.
Conclusion
The accelerometer detects changes in velocity whenever either the speed or direction is changed.

Unit 1 Lesson 3
Review, p. 34
1. B 2. D 3. C
4. A 5. D 6. B
7. Electrical energy is used to produce sound energy.
8. Electrical energy is used to produce light energy.
9. No. The pitcher does not apply force to the ball after it leaves his or her hand.

Doing Work, p. 35
1. the hiker
2. the climber
3. 80,000 joules
4. 80,000 joules
5. The hiker used less force and traveled a longer distance, while the climber used a greater force and traveled a shorter distance.

Juggling Energy, p. 36
1. potential energy
2. kinetic energy
3. The kinetic energy decreases as the pin slows down.

Answer Key cont'd.

4. The potential energy decreases as the pin falls back down.

5. potential and kinetic energy

6. mechanical energy

Unscrambling Energy, p. 37

1. heat

2. sound

3. light

4. joule

5. thermal

6. kinetic

Answer: nuclear

Experiment: Changing Energy, p. 39

Results and Analysis

1. Sketches will vary.

2. The ball bearing has the most potential energy at the start.

Conclusion

Changes between potential and kinetic energy occur during a roller coaster ride.

Unit 2 Lesson 4

Review, p. 45

1. C   **2.** B   **3.** A

4. C   **5.** B   **6.** D

7. The nucleus is the "control" center as it directs many of the cell's functions.

8. Microscopes were first needed so that cells could be seen and studied.

Cells I, p. 46

1. nucleus   **2.** cell

3. chlorophyll   **4.** cell membrane

5. nucleus   **6.** cytoplasm

7. photosynthesis   **8.** bacteria

9. cell wall   **10.** cell wall

Cells II, p. 47

Strange Creatures of the Deep, p. 48

1. C   **2.** D   **3.** A

Experiment: Cell Size, p. 50

Results and Analysis

1.

Length of side	Volume	Surface Area
1 inch	1 cubic inch	6 square inches
2 inches	8 cubic inches	24 square inches

Answer Key cont'd.

2.

Length of side	Surface area/volume
1 inch	$\frac{6}{1}$
2 inches	$\frac{3}{1}$

3. The smaller cube has the larger surface area to volume ratio.

Conclusions

1. The surface area to volume ratio gets smaller as the cube gets bigger.

2. The cell membrane of the smaller cell because it has more surface area for foods to pass through and enter the cell.

Unit 2 Lesson 5
Review, p. 55

1. C   **2.** B   **3.** D
4. A   **5.** C   **6.** B

7. In external fertilization, a sperm fertilizes an egg outside the female's body. In internal fertilization, the sperm fertilizes an egg inside the female's body.

8. Reproduction provides for the continuity of the species.

Unscrambling Reproduction, p. 56

1. SEXUAL   **2.** ASEXUAL
3. STAMEN   **4.** ANTHER
5. BUDDING   **6.** FISSION
7. REGENERATION   **8.** FERTILIZATION

Twins, p. 57

1. Identical twins have identical DNA because they develop from a single zygote that divides and then splits.

2. Fraternal twins do not have identical DNA because they develop from two separate zygotes.

The Mathematics of Reproduction, p. 58

1. 456 eggs   **2.** 8 sets
3. 6 sets   **4.** 3.75%

Experiment: A Model of Bacterial Reproduction, p. 59
Procedure

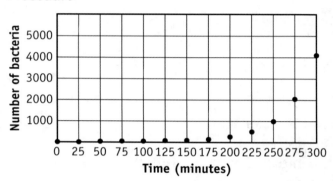

Results and Analysis
4096 bacterial cells

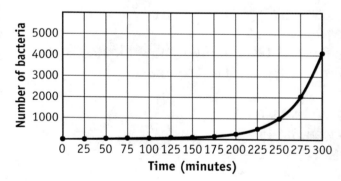

Conclusion
The number of bacteria increases slowly at first, but then rises sharply.

Unit 2 Lesson 6
Review, p. 64

1. B   **2.** D   **3.** C
4. A   **5.** C   **6.** A

7. An innate behavior depends on genes. A learned behavior depends on experience and observations.

Answer Key cont'd.

8. Hibernation is the slowing down of life processes in preparation for cold weather. Estivation is the slowing down of life processes in preparation for hot weather.

Hibernation and Estivation, p. 65
1. The animals are more likely to hibernate in Glacier National Park because the temperatures during the winter months drop below freezing.
2. December, January, and February

Unscrambling Behavior, p. 66
1. Behave yourself. 2. innate behavior
3. defensive   4. hibernation

Imprinting, p. 67
1. B   2. D   3. C   4. A

Experiment: Bug Behavior, p. 69
Results and Analysis
More sow bugs should collect in the dark side.
Conclusion
1. Sow bugs prefer the dark as evidenced by more bugs collecting in that side of the shoe box.
2. This is a defensive behavior as it protects them from being seen by predators.

Unit 2 Lesson 7
Review, p. 73
1. B   2. D   3. A   4. C
5. D   6. A   7. B
8. Answers will vary but should show a correct sequence.

9. The number of prairie dogs, squirrels, and insects would increase. Their increased numbers would affect the organisms they feed upon and the organisms that feed upon them.

Finding Food, p. 74
Check that students marked the correct path.

A Population and Ecosystem Crossword Puzzle, p. 75
Across
4. food web
6. pyramid
7. carnivore
8. herbivore
9. ecosystem
Down
1. producer
2. food chain
3. decomposers
5. omnivore

Constructing a Food Chain, p. 76
1. lettuce → rabbit → weasel
2. plant remains → woodmouse → owl

An Energy Pyramid, p. 77
1. the bird and the plant
2. the coyotes and the prairie dogs
3. No. There are more coyotes shown than can be supported by the number of prairie dogs shown. There are more prairie dogs shown than there is grass.
4. Show more prairie dogs and more grass in the energy pyramid.

Answer Key cont'd.

Experiment: Making Your Own Food, p. 79
Results and Analysis
The acidity level increases as the milk sours.
Conclusion
The proteins can be isolated from the liquid part of milk to make cheese.

Unit 2 Lesson 8
Review, p. 84
1. D   2. C   3. A
4. B   5. D   6. C
7. Euglena is classified in the protist kingdom because of its plantlike and animal-like features.
8. A scientific name leaves no doubt as to what organism is being discussed or studied.

A Branching Diagram, p. 85
1. The lion and the house cat are more closely related because they share the most characteristics.
2. giving birth to live young
3. platypus; It shares the fewest characteristics with the house cat.
4. ability to purr

Classification Diagrams, p. 86
1. A   2. B
3. Organisms in group 4 share characteristics with members of both groups 2 and 5.
4. Level 7 would represent a kingdom as it is the broadest and includes all the others.

Amazing Survivors, p. 87
1. archaebacteria; These organisms can survive extremely harsh conditions.

2. They formed spores like the bacteria that survived in amber.
3. Yes. This passage describes bacteria, which are prokaryotes, that have survived extremely harsh conditions.

A Kingdom Word Search, p. 88

```
B O O O F B H R Z V I A W J A G Q B J
B Q X L H B T T A A N Q G J Y M H X J W
B B Z I B Z O R A I K R O X E G N I J O
Z Z P M R R K W M K E D G T T X I P P U
T Y E T P T G A E J T Q Z K L I C U R J
U N D O U R L I S G N A E R C B Z K O P
W Y A S L E H F P A B M O B G C A T T I
U O O L Y E U U Z N S U G N U F Y F I X
R C J U P A K B O I L F E E N X N P S D
X J W F E H E C A X Z H I B N Q H M T X
A D G U Y W U B Q C I Y H J K J L V L F
E A B A Y E A U V E T M M C W I M L X D
S I V U P L I X N R Q E I O B K P E R E
L S F K O H X D H P P I R A Q D C U H O
W G S S Q A V I C G V R G I H H L M E G
J A R C H A E B A C T E R I A Y L Q W N
R P G U Z Q Q P V A N T F V P P W P L N
U Y B B J W Y U B M F Z A G D W P A Q B
B R Q D U X U L Q C K N J S O B N U V A
Q R R E K B Q I J G H V O R A Y B Q K L
```

Experiment: Developing a Classification System, p. 89
The systems that students develop will vary depending on the characteristic chosen at each step.

Answer Key cont'd.

Unit 3 Lesson 9
Review, p. 94
1. B   2. B   3. A
4. D   5. C   6. B
7. They examine magma that rises from the mantle to the surface.
8. The ozone layer blocks most of the harmful ultraviolet light from reaching Earth.
9. A tectonic plate is a large block of lithosphere that moves on the magma beneath it.

Complete the Sentences, p. 95
1. hydrothermal vent   2. core
3. thermosphere   4. atmosphere
5. crust   6. lithosphere
7. tectonic plate   8. asthenosphere
9. mantle   10. Magma

How Far Down Must You Go?, p. 96
1. 2900 km
2. 2950 km
3. about 6380 km
4. continental crust because of its thickness
5. 150 km

Unscrambling Earth, p. 97
1. continental crust
2. tectonic plate
3. lithosphere
4. hydrothermal vent
5. aluminum

Godzilla, p. 98
1. C   2. D   3. A   4. C

Experiment: The Atmosphere, p. 100
Results and Analysis
1. gas bubbles
2. The flame went out because the carbon dioxide gas flowed down the trough.

Conclusion
The atmosphere is a fluid because the gases that make up the atmosphere flow.

Unit 3 Lesson 10
Review, p. 105
1. C   2. B   3. A
4. D   5. B   6. C
7. The inner planets are closer to the sun, made of rocky material, and are smaller than the outer planets which are called gas giants.
8. Some of the particles in the solar nebula stuck together and formed larger particles. This process continued and eventually formed the planets.

The Planets I, p. 106
1. They are the inner planets.
2. in a counterclockwise direction
3. Mercury is much closer to the sun.
4. No. Mars's orbit is elliptical and not circular. As a result, it is closer to the sun at some points during its revolution.
5. Mercury is the closest planet to the sun.

The Planets II, p. 107
1. They are the outer planets.

Answer Key cont'd.

2. Pluto is different because it is the smallest planet, it is probably made of rock and ice, it has not been visited by a NASA mission, and its orbit crosses that of Neptune, which caused Pluto to be reclassified as a "dwarf planet."
3. Jupiter, because it is closest to the sun.
4. Neptune, because it is farthest from the sun.

Comparing the Planets, p. 108

1. A person would weigh more on both Neptune and Jupiter because their gravity is greater than Earth's.
2. The inner planets are smaller and have a greater density than the outer planets.
3. Earth and Venus are similar in size, density, and the force of gravity.
4. Saturn has a smaller density than Earth. Although Saturn has a larger volume, it contains much less mass. Density depends on mass and volume.

Planet X, p. 109

1. This was the way in which he used parallax to determine if an object in space moves.
2. Scientists always repeat their procedures to make sure of their results.
3. Pluto is very small and the farthest planet from Earth.

Experiment: Blasting Off, p. 111

Results and Analysis

1. The force propels the canister upward.
2. Answers will vary.

Conclusion

A simple model of a rocket can be built using a film canister, vinegar, and baking soda.

4500596076 0607 2016
Printed in the U.S.A.